Made in Liverpool

Liverpool Pottery and Porcelain 1700 - 1850

The Seventh Exhibition from the Northern Ceramic Society
27 June – 19 September 1993
Walker Art Gallery
Liverpool

NATIONAL MUSEUMS & GALLERIES
· ON MERSEYSIDE ·

MADE IN LIVERPOOL
Liverpool Pottery and Porcelain 1700 – 1850

© Board of Trustees of the National Museums
& Galleries on Merseyside and Individual Authors

Edited E. Myra Brown & Terence A. Lockett
Design T. Doyle
Photography D. Flower
Printed in Great Britain 1993

ISBN 0 906367 63 8
British Library Cataloguing-in-Publication Data
Available

Cover illustrations:
'La Nourrice', porcelain figure of a seated nurse breast-feeding a child. Richard Chaffers c. 1758-60 (Cat. 99).

CONTENTS

ACKNOWLEDGEMENTS

On behalf of the Trustees of the National Museums and Galleries on Merseyside and the Northern Ceramic Society we would like to acknowledge the co-operation of many people without whose generosity the Exhibition and this accompanying catalogue would not have been possible.

B. Allaker
R.G. & S. Allum
A. Atterbury
J.F. Becker
S.M. Beddoe
J.W. & R. Bentley
G. Blake Roberts
J.P. Bradshaw
J.S.W. Brierley
The Trustees of
The British Museum
D. & H. Burke
M. Caron Delion
T.E. Crabtree
F. Davies
P.F. & B. Davies
A.M. Dawson
B.P. Downing
D. Drakard
G.C. Fisk
G.A. Godden
The Granada Foundation
B.D. Griffin
P.A. Halfpenny

W.W. Hamilton Foyn
R. & E. Hampson
J. Harrop
J. Hewitt
M. & L. Hillis
P. & K. Holdway
D. Holgate
P.G. Hyland
M. Ironside
J. Jameson
R. Jellicoe
S. & G. Jenkins
P. King
J.K. & M. A. Linacre
Liverpool Record Office
(Liverpool City Libraries)
B.P. Lomax
T. Lonton
T. Markin
R. Meldrum
B. Pain
B.H. & S.F.G. Parkinson
B.E. & M. Peers
M. & R. Pulver

D.L. Rockwell
Royal Pavilion, Art Gallery & Museums, Brighton
B. & E. Schofield
C. Simpson
A. Smith
K. Staniland
E.N. Stretton
City Museum & Art Gallery, Stoke-on-Trent
M. Thacker
A. & H. Thomas
S. Walsh
B. Watney
Williamson Art Gallery & Museum, Birkenhead

We would especially like to thank Theresa Doyle, Designer; David Flower, Photographer; Lynne Kelly, Conservator and Sue Lunt, Assistant Curator for their help in the preparation and mounting of the Exhibition. We also thank the lenders who wish to remain anonymous.

E. Myra Brown, Curator of Ceramics

Terence A. Lockett, President, Northern Ceramic Society.

FOREWORD

The National Museums and Galleries on Merseyside are delighted to work with the Northern Ceramic Society in presenting the first major exhibition to be devoted to the full range of historic pottery and porcelain made and decorated in Liverpool. This is the first exhibition we have staged together, and sets new standards of scholarship in Liverpool ceramics. Its purpose is to reassess our knowledge at a time when excavated fragments, documentary evidence and renewed study of the wares themselves are causing a shift in perspective.

Collectors and curators know that our knowledge of the past is changing continually, that one generation's comfortable certainties will be overturned by the next as a result of new discoveries. It is just as vital to keep one's knowledge up to date in this field as it is in high-technology business. This catalogue gives the 'state of the art' in Liverpool ceramics. A prudent caution in making attributions can ensure that, despite subsequent additions to knowledge, a catalogue remains a reliable guide. The catalogues of previous Northern Ceramic Society exhibitions have achieved textbook status. We are sure that this one will stand alongside them.

It is appropriate that this exhibition is a joint venture, because it reflects the nature of the work behind it. The catalogue is edited jointly by the Society's President, Terry Lockett and NMGM's Curator of Ceramics,

Myra Brown and we would like to thank them for their scholarly work which has made it such a significant publication. The collections in the Liverpool Museum continue to play a crucial role in the pioneering research carried out by members of the Society. Pots from members' collections are shown in the exhibition side by side with those from NMGM's own holdings, including most importantly the sherds excavated on the sites where the pots were made.

We are grateful to the Trustees of The British Museum; to the Royal Pavilion, Art Gallery & Museums, Brighton; to the Williamson Art Gallery & Museum, Birkenhead; and to the City Museum & Art Gallery, Stoke-on-Trent, for lending important pieces. The exhibits are displayed in elegant new showcases which have been specially designed in keeping with the architecture of the Walker Art Gallery, and we are most grateful to the Granada Foundation for the initial grant which has made this possible. Finally we are grateful to all those members of the Northern Ceramic Society who have agreed to be parted from their pots for so long.

Richard A. Foster, Director
Julian B. Treuherz, Keeper of Art Galleries
National Museums & Galleries on Merseyside

INTRODUCTION

This is the seventh Exhibition organised by the Northern Ceramic Society in association with a northern Museum in the 21 years of the Society's existence. All have been deemed successful in one way or another. In the case of several of them, the catalogues have entered the literature of ceramic history as important contributions to the scholarship of the subject. We hope that this catalogue on Liverpool ceramics will prove to be of equal importance, though undoubtedly the subject is, in many respects, the most difficult we have undertaken.

Liverpool as the subject of 'your next Exhibition' was first mooted in 1989 by Lionel Burman then Curator of Decorative Arts at Liverpool Museum. The Committee of the Society agreed to the suggestion after we had further discussion with Myra Brown, who since the retirement of Mr. Burman in April 1992 has taken full responsibility for the Museum's side of the Exhibition. The decision was not taken lightly for the ceramics of Liverpool present a serious challenge to anyone who genuinely wishes to make a scholarly contribution to the correct attribution of the wares made in the city. We were encouraged by the success of the Exhibition organised by Cherry Grey at the Warrington Museum in 1983, *'Herculaneum - the Last Liverpool Pottery'*. Thanks to the enthusiasm of Mrs Grey and the dedicated help of the late Nancy Gunson, this Exhibition had stimulated much interest, and considerable progress had been made in the correct attribution of Herculaneum porcelain. Perhaps the same would be possible in 1993 for some of the other difficult areas of attribution such as pre-Herculaneum creamware, Liverpool pearlware and most especially the thorny thicket of Liverpool porcelain?

Those who come to the Exhibition will have to judge for themselves whether any progress has been made in any direction. Those of us who have had a hand in organising the display have their own ideas. There has certainly been no real progress in correctly identifying creamwares actually made in Liverpool before the marked wares of Herculaneum. Not a single marked piece from the Okill factory or any of the other factories of which we have documentary knowledge has been identified. This is a disappointment. We are able, thanks to the generosity of our lenders, to show a goodly few examples of creamware, and other types of ceramic which were printed in the city. These include some fine delft tiles, Worcester and Longton Hall as well as Liverpool porcelain, and a splendid display of Herculaneum printed patterns. The story of the development of printing in Liverpool is told by David Drakard in his essay in this catalogue.

The situation for pearlware is much the same as that for creamware. Despite considerable efforts at identification, there are very few blue painted pearlware pieces, which can with any certainty be attributed to Liverpool potteries. We have noticed a growing tendency to make totally tendentious attributions of such pearlwares.

Pearlware teapot and cover, underglaze painted. Herculaneum factory, c.1805 (Cat. 220).

We can only stress that no marked blue painted pearl-wares are known, nor, as is the case with delftware is there any convincing evidence for a particular 'Liverpool style' of decoration. In this respect the Exhibition has much in common with that at Stoke-on-Trent in 1986 on Creamware and Pearlware. Those of us responsible for that display felt that a significant advance had been made because, in the absence of positive evidence, we were not able glibly to label the wares 'Leeds', 'Melbourne', 'Flint Potworks, Liverpool' or whatever. This scrupulousness was not appreciated by everyone. There were some who complained that they 'learned nothing', or that we had overturned much previous connoisseurship. We hope the point has now been understood. We are disappointed not to be able to fill the cases with authentic Liverpool-made creamware from the 1760s, 70s and 80s, or pearlwares from the 1780-1810 period. Let us hope that in the next twenty years archaeology will come to the aid of researchers in this area, as it has with regard to the porcelain.

We could have filled the cases several times over with porcelain manufactured in Liverpool. The very recent advances in our knowledge of the true nature of the groups of wares heretofore attributed to William Reid and William Ball are chronicled by Roderick Jellicoe in his essay. The migration of these groups from Liverpool has been partly balanced by the progress made, based on the researches of Dr. Maurice Hillis, in the groups of wares now attributed to John Pennington and to the enigmatic 'H.P.' group. We have been especially fortunate to have had the co-operation of such a distinguished group of advisers as (in alphabetical order), Brian Allaker, Dr. Peter Bradshaw, Dr. Maurice Hillis, Dr. Geoffrey Godden, Roderick Jellicoe, Trevor Markin, Prof. Alan Smith, Norman Stretton, and Dr. Bernard Watney. We are deeply grateful to them all. Their expertise and kindness in loaning wares has been of inestimable value in this most important section of the Exhibition.

Exhibitions of this kind are always co-operative ventures. Our general membership responded splendidly to our appeal for wares. But as always we felt there were gaps. Several members, some named above, but others - both institutions and private individuals - whose names simply appear in the list of lenders gave us the free run of their collections. Myra Brown and I are extremely grateful for this facility for it enables us to make the Exhibition more representative of the Liverpool range without doing violence to the objective that this is an Exhibition of wares offered by members of the Northern Ceramic Society. Of the institutions who have lent wares, two in particular deserve our especial thanks, the Williamson Art Gallery and Museum, Birkenhead in the person of the Curator Colin Simpson, and the National Museums and Art Galleries on Merseyside in Liverpool. Myra Brown and the recently appointed Curator of Decorative Art, Robin Emmerson have been continually co-operative as the various advisors have come into the Study and Reserve collections and selected objects 'which must be included'. We hope that we have satisfied most of these requests.

It is simply not possible in an Exhibition limited to some 250 pieces - the maximum that could reasonably be accommodated and catalogued - to cover all facets of the subject equally. One aspect of Liverpool ceramics which has not been treated as a special topic on this

Porcelain coffee pot and cover, over and underglaze painted. John Pennington c.1775-85 (Cat. 154).

occasion is that of the export of wares, in particular to the United States of America. We include one or two pieces printed with American subjects, but these are only a token sample of a huge and profitable trade in wares for the American market, many made in Liverpool, but many more made in Staffordshire and elsewhere and exported through this thriving port.

An interesting, unpublished, account of a voyage from New York to Dublin and Liverpool in 1824, was noted and transcribed by Isabel Lockett from the archive at the Henry Francis du Pont Winterthur Museum and Library in Delaware. The diary is signed 'R.K.G.' (possibly for Rufus King Gilman). The relevant parts read:

'After being a week in the City [Dublin] *I crossed over to Liverpool to pass a few days there and in the vicinity....there is not much at Liverpool that is particularly interesting to the stranger and the streets are generally narrow and the buildings ordinary. The town increases rapidly and for commerce stands*

'Part of Lord Street, with St. George's Church in the Distance' from *'Lancashire Illustrated'*, 1832.
Drawn by Harwood, engraved by B. Winkles

unrivalled in the kingdom. The Exchange buildings are said to be the most extensive in the world created solely for commercial purposes. In the area formed by the Exchange buildings and town hall is a Nelson's monument executed in Bronze some years since at an immense expense....the Docks at Liverpool are very extensive and they are still increasing them...
I visited the Herculaneum Pottery while at Liverpool and saw the whole process of manufacturing the crockery and Porcelain - the clay is br't to town by the Canale and by mixing with water is made so thin as to pass through a fine muslin seive - a quantity of flint burnt and made equally fine is then mixed with it and the water is boiled away and the clay is then passed several times through a machine to work it, when it is cut in small pieces for the different articles. Round ware, such as plates bowls etc are shaped on a stand in the manner stone ware is made in America and when a little dried is turned in lathe, and it is while in the lathe that the brown lines that we see on enamelled ware are put on [Strictly speaking, dipped and turned ware] *Oval tea Pots etc are made in moulds of Plaster of Paris - the ordinary blue Printing is done by taking the Impression from a Copper Plate on a thin paper which is immediately placed on the ware - this is done before glazing - another kind of printing is done by taking a Copper Plate impression in Oil on a sheet of glutinous substance which is then laid on the article to be printed - a brown or red colour is then added which adheres to the Oil - the fine landscapes, Gilding etc is done with the pencil, as well as the flowering on the enamelled ware. Some of the Porcelain is burnt three or four times once after each addition of Painting or Gilding - the Machinery is all operated and the boiling done by steam....* [He continues later]*...Manchester is a smokey*

gloomy place & it requires a gale of wind to give them a clear atmosphere...' apart from the derogatory remarks about Manchester – a fascinating and succinct account of Herculaneum in its prime.

View of the Herculaneum Pottery, watercolour by Joseph Mayer, 1825.

Not all Americans appreciated the Herculaneum Pottery. W.C. Prince writing in '*Pottery & Porcelain*' in 1878 comments:

'*Many of the Herculaneum cream-coloured wares have prints relating to America. These have no special value as ceramic specimens, but are curious and interesting. They are in general of ungainly shapes and the prints are poor specimens of the art ...*' We trust that visitors to the Exhibition will not echo Prince's condemnation!

Let me stress that this a members' Exhibition. The firm basis has been provided by over 50 members of the Society who have generously offered to be separated from their treasures for over a year. We are immensely grateful to all of those named in the Acknowledgements. We also offer especial thanks to all those who have provided their time and expertise freely in writing essays for the catalogue and acting as advisers throughout the enterprise. We also owe particular thanks to the Director, Richard Foster and to Julian Treuherz, Keeper of Art Galleries for their full co-operation and support in assisting us to stage the Exhibition in the splendid setting of the Walker Art Gallery. Professor Alan Smith has been associated with the study of Liverpool ceramics for well over thirty years and his standard book on the subject was published in 1970. He has been most supportive of our efforts and given invaluable advice, as well as writing two sections of the catalogue. He is a founder committee member of the NCS and it is a great joy to us all that he has accepted our invitation to formally open this Exhibition on 26 June, 1993.

Finally, the thanks of all members of the Society are due to Myra Brown. She has worked unstintingly for the past two years – and managed to start a family at the same time – to create a display, and to prepare a catalogue which will both stand the test of time and yet be the stimulus to further research into one of the most fascinating of topics – the Pottery and Porcelain of Liverpool. We are immensely grateful to Myra for her knowledge and dedication.

Terence A. Lockett,
President,
Northern Ceramic Society

LIVERPOOL – THE CITY AND ITS INDUSTRIES

In 1700 Liverpool, situated on the banks of the River Mersey, was a small port of barely 5,000 inhabitants. By 1850 it was a large and still-expanding town of well over a quarter of a million people. Brooke, writing in 1852, summarised Liverpool's rapid development:

'During the present, and a considerable part of the last century, Liverpool has advanced in commercial greatness and prosperity, with a rapidity which is most unprecedented; and from being a place comparatively unimportant, it has become one of the most populous and prosperous towns in Europe.' [1]

Its geographical situation, near the mouth of a wide river on the west coast of mainland Britain, was undoubtedly the key to its future prosperity. The natural tidal inlet, or *'pool, which has been appropriately called the cradle of Liverpool'*,[2] on the eastern shore of the Mersey estuary, created a convenient and reasonably secure harbour for vessels.

Prior to 1700 Liverpool existed as a small fishing and trading village with agriculture in the surrounding area providing an additional source of income. Liverpool itself is not mentioned in the Domesday Book although other places in the vicinity are. In 1207 Liverpool had developed sufficiently to be granted a Charter by King John, giving it the privileges and liberties of a free port. Another Charter was granted in 1229 by Henry III by which Liverpool became an 'incorporated' borough.[3] But for many years, if not centuries, Liverpool, described as *'a creek of the port of Chester'*, [4]

was a sub-port of Chester on the River Dee, trading with Ireland, the Isle of Man and N. Wales. Its main imports were leather, flax and linen yarn, wool, salt herrings and other foodstuffs; its exports salt, iron, copper, hops, cloth, alum and soap.[5] In 1565, Liverpool consisted of 7 main streets inhabited by 185 householders or cottagers and owning just 12 barks or boats.[6] By 1700, 102 ships are recorded as trading with the town.[7] Over the next 150 years Liverpool was to emerge from these humble beginnings to become the second largest port in the country.

Before considering the trades and industries of Liverpool, one of which is the subject of this exhibition, one should perhaps gain an impression of the look of the town and an idea of the conditions in which people lived and worked.

By 1725 the population of Liverpool had increased to about 11,000 inhabitants. These people were housed in some 50 streets, alleys and courts which lay clustered along the low-lying ground beside the water front.[8] An impression of the size of the town is given by Brooke:

'On the south side of Church Street there was a large orchard and one of the streets opened into the country; Bold Street did not exist and Clayton Square, though laid out, had only a few houses erected on it: part of the east side of Whitechapel was bounded by a hawthorne hedge.'[9]

The small town was surrounded by open country-side, scattered with farms and orchards. Here and there

Delftware punch bowl, in-glaze painted. Liverpool 1770 (Cat. 13).

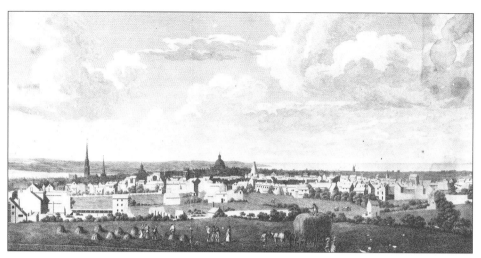

'*A View of the Town and Harbour of Leverpool*'(detail) Published by George Perry 1770, drawn by Michael Angelo Rooker, engraved by Edward Rooker.

with no through ventilation. Even worse were the numerous cellar-dwellings in which many unfortunate families were forced to live. A report in 1789 gives a graphic description of what conditions were really like:

In consequence of the immense quantities of rain which fell, the cellars in Whitechapel and the adjacent streets were almost deluged with water so that the wretched tenants of these miserable places were absolutely driven out of them.[11]

were situated the homes of the wealthier citizens who sought to combine the advantages of proximity to the town with the more salubrious rural surroundings.

The town itself consisted largely of narrow, ill-drained and insanitary streets, as only the principal roads were paved along the centre of the carriageway. The dirty conditions of the streets is frequently referred to in the town records. On 24 October 1719 the Council resolved to grant a contract to Alderman Gildart and Mr Samuel Done *'to provide proper carts and carriages and therewith to take away all the muck and dirt in the streets and passages of the town twice every week, viz. every Monday and Thursday'*.[10]

The housing conditions in which the majority of the people lived were equally cramped and unhealthy. Many of the houses were of the old back-to-back type

Enfield, commenting on a population survey in 1773, stated *'It appears from hence that the inhabitants of Liverpool live more closely crowded together than in most other towns......It is probable that there is no place in Great Britain, except London and Edinburgh, which contains so many inhabitants in so small a compass'*.[12] Living in these over-crowded conditions, ignorant of basic hygiene and undernourished, it is no wonder that epidemics and diseases had such a devastating effect on the population. The average life expectancy in Liverpool was 30 years. That death was an all too frequent visitor, especially for the impoverished, is summed up on a remarkable inscription on a gravestone, dated 1789, in St. Nicholas' church-yard, which reads:

'This Town's a Corporation full of crooked streets
Death is the Market-place where all men meets;
If Life was merchandise that men could buy,
The rich wou'd alwaye live, the poor must die'.[13]

It is therefore surprising that Enfield also thought *'Leverpool one of the healthiest places in the kingdome, in proportion to the number of the inhabitants'*. This he attributed to the climate and *'the mildness of the air, the antiseptic effluvia of pitch and tar, the acid exhalations from the sea, the frequent brisk gales of wind and the daily visitations of the tides'*.[14] Perhaps he was trying not to paint a too gloomy picture of the place!

An account of his visit to Liverpool by Samuel Curwen, Judge of the Admiralty, in June 1780, perhaps gives us a more unbiased description of the place:

'Entered the City of Liverpool, so celebrated for its commercial character, houses by a great majority, in middling and lower style, few rising above that mark; streets long, narrow and crooked and dirty in an emminent degree. During our short abode here we scarcely saw a well-dressed person, nor half a dozen gentlemen's carriages........ The whole complexion nautical and so infinitely below our expectations, that naught but the thoughts of the few hours we had to pass here render it tolerable'.[15]

Against this back-drop of squalor and poor living-conditions, Liverpool continued to develop and expand its trade – both to and from foreign ports. As well as being a gateway for the import and export of raw materials and finished goods, the 18th century also saw the growth of its own local industries. The prosperity of the town and port were interdependent.

Improvements to the Dock system throughout the 1700s enabled Liverpool's maritime trade to develop rapidly. In 1709 an Act of Parliament was passed for *'making a convenient Dock or Bason, at Leverpoole, for the security of all ships trading to and from the said Port'*.[16] The first wet dock, later known as the Old Dock was opened in 1715 and in 1737 a dry dock, called Salthouse Dock, was built. Later in the century, in 1761, as increased trade demanded more dock accommodation, another Act of Parliament ordered the construction of a

'The South West Prospect of Liverpoole, in the County Palatine of Lancaster' (detail), S. & N. Buck, 1728.

new wet dock, named George's Dock, lighthouses and piers. As an aid to shipping, the Bidston Lighthouse, on the opposite bank of the Mersey, was begun in 1771. This structure is recorded on both pottery and glass (Cat.181 & 183). By 1800 the trade of the port had expanded to accomodate 4,786 ships, with an aggregate burthen of almost half a million tons.[17]

Inland communications also improved dramatically during the 18th century with the building of toll roads, canals and canalized rivers like the Sankey Brook canal built in 1757 to carry coal from St. Helens to Liverpool. Navigational improvements were made to the Rivers Mersey, Irwell and Weaver and the cutting of the Mersey-Trent canal, completed in 1777, and the Staffordshire-Worcester canal brought further benefit. The canal system especially linked Liverpool with much of the North and Midlands of the country. It enabled the transport of coal and textiles from Lancashire, salt from Cheshire, pottery from Staffordshire, iron and metal from the Midlands and woollen goods from Yorkshire. The steam-powered railway of the early 19th century, begun by the opening of the Liverpool-Manchester Railway in 1830, was to enhance communications still further. Liverpool's merchants and shipowners were not slow to profit from this advantageous position.

'A View of the Custom House, Taken from Traffords Wyent' Published in 1774, drawn by P.P. Burdett, engraved by E. Rooker.

From about 1730 one of the most lucrative 18th century trades was the Slave Trade or 'Africa Trade' as it was also known. Prior to that date an occasional ship had sailed, in 1709 one ship is recorded, but in 1730, 15 ships sailed for Africa to collect their human cargoes.

Until then, this trade, described as an *'odious and inhuman source of emolument'*,[18] had mainly been in the hands of Bristol, London and Glasgow but over the years Liverpool was to dominate them all. By 1751, 53 slavers were sailing from the port and this number was to increase to 106 in 1771, and to 149 in 1798 when the height of the trade was reached. The ships ran a 'commmercial triangle' comprising the carrying of muskets, gunpowder, spirits and cotton goods to West Africa, where they were bartered for slaves; the transportation of these slaves to the West Indies and America, and from their sale, the purchase of cargoes of sugar, coffee and rum from the West Indies and raw cotton and tobacco from America, for shipment back to England.

Other trades and industries developed as a direct result of trade with the West Indies and America – sugar and tobacco refining were two of the most important ones. The foundation of the sugar industry in Liverpool can be traced as far back as the 17th century when, in about 1668, Sir Edward Moore recorded that *'one Mr Smith, a great sugar baker at London, a man, as report goes, with forty thousand pounds'* was interested in a site for a sugar house in Liverpool. Sir Edward also foretold that sugar would *'bring a trade of at least forty thousand pounds a year from Barbadoes, which formerly this town never knew'*.[19] The first sugar house was built in the early 1670s by Richard Cleaveland and Dan Danvers. By 1773 the industry had grown further and Enfield records that there were then 8 sugar houses: *'Sugar-baking and refining is a business which, ever since the increase of foreign Commerce, has been carried on in this place. There are at present eight Sugar Houses, in which about 6,000 hogsheads of sugar are annually refined'*.[20]

The import of tobacco is recorded as early as 1648 when a duty of £3 on 30 tons of tobacco was paid by James Jenkinson, master of the *'Friendship'* which brought it.[21] As trade with America grew so did the import of tobacco. In 1770, 5441 hogsheads of tobacco were imported from Virginia and Maryland. Further expansion of the trade resulted, in 1795, in the erection of a warehouse at the Kings Dock for the storage of up to 7000 hogsheads of tobacco. In 1812 an even larger one was constructed.

Other trades directly linked to the sea also flourished including whaling and fishing. The first vessel which sailed for the 'Greenland trade' as whaling was then known, was the *'Golden Lion'* in 1750.[22] The fishing trade was also extensive. Enfield lists 44 different species of fish caught in the Mersey,[23] and Brooke comments that *'the capture of fish, especially cod and herring, was occasionally very great'*.[24] Resulting industries developed and *'a building for extracting the oil from the fat and blubber of whales was erected at the South End of the Queens Dock'*.[25] By 1775 six herring-curing houses are recorded in Liverpool, mainly supplied with herring from the Isle of Man.

In addition to the trades already mentioned were salt refining; seed crushing; clock, watch and file-making; ship-building; rope and sail-making; glass-making; and brick, pipe and pottery-making. In 1773 there were 2 glass houses, a copperas and iron-works, a salt works, 15 roperies, 36 public breweries and *'in or very near the town 27 windmills, 16 for grinding corn, 9 for grinding colours, 1 for rasping and grinding dyers wood and 1 for raising water at the salt-works'*.[26]

This exhibition concerns itself with the products of one of those trades - the pottery and porcelain of Liverpool. It is not known exactly when pottery-making first began in the town itself. Most of the earliest records relating to potting date from the 17th century but usually refer to the production of bricks and tiles. Gatty records that *'there is one in 1618 concerning the getting of marl on the common by one Mossock of Toxteth Park'*[27] and a later reference of 1692 gives permission to a Mr William Praddock to *'build a shead upon ye Common to make or mould Bricks or Tyle'*.[28]

Along with the bricks and tiles it seems likely that utilitarian pottery such as mugs, jugs and bowls was also being made in Liverpool, as well as in the surrounding villages such as Prescot and Ormskirk. A quantity of early mottled lead-glazed ware has been unearthed during demolition and roadworks in the city centre including a complete earthenware jug of about 1700.[29] These pieces could well be the products of local pothouses. Pipe-making, an off-shoot of the tobacco trade, was certainly carrried on in 17th century Liverpool. In the Holt & Gregson MSS, quoted by Gatty, we read *'There are seven pipe manufactories in Liverpool and about sixty men employed by the masters in this business and about as many women, since every labourer has a female to finish off'*.[30]

The earliest record to the production of tin-glazed earthenware or 'delftware' in Liverpool appeared in the London *'Post Boy'* on the 23rd May 1710 :

'The Corporation of Liverpool in Lancashire have encouraged there a Manufactory of all sorts of white and painted pots and other vessels and Tiles in imitation of China, both for inland and outland Trade, which will be speedily ready and sold at reasonable rates'.[31]

Porcelain bough pot, overglaze painted and gilded. Herculaneum factory 1811 (Cat. 262).

Further documentary evidence indicates that a Mr Richard Holt accompanied by several potters from Southwark near London came to Liverpool to start this pottery.

Local clays were not suited to the making of delft-ware which required a light-firing clay. In 1710 Richard Holt is recorded as obtaining his clay from Northern Ireland. Over forty years later in 1751, 641 tons of it were imported from Carrickfergus in Northern Ireland.[32] Interestingly, a ship *'The Hope'* is listed as trading between Liverpool and Carrickfergus, probably carrying clay. [33] One wonders whether it is the same ship portrayed on a Liverpool delftware ship bowl of 1763 (Cat. 4)? Other raw materials for the making of pottery and porcelain were imported by ship to Liverpool, either for use in the local pothouses or for transporting to the Staffordshire factories.

From these beginnings the industry continued to thrive and by the middle of the century, around 12 pot-works were producing delftware, including at least two on Shaw's Brow (now William Brown Street). (See essay on *'Liverpool Earthenwares and Stonewares'*).

The Liverpool potters were not immune to the demand for porcelain, especially teawares, by the growing merchant classes. During the second half of the 18th century seven sites in Liverpool were involved in the production of porcelain. (See essay on *'Liverpool Porcelains'*). The earliest factories were those of Richard Chaffers and Samuel Gilbody on Shaw's Brow: both are thought to have started making porcelain around 1754. The first advertisement for Chaffers' porcelain appears on 3rd December 1756:

'The Porcelain, or China ware, made by Messrs. Richard Chaffers & Co. is sold nowhere in this Town but at their Manufactory on Shaw's Brow. Considerable Abatement for Exportation and to all Wholesale Dealers. N.B. All the Ware is proved with boyling Water before it's expos'd to sale'.[34]

The size of the pottery industry by the mid 18th century is indicated in the certificate signed by Alderman Shaw and Samuel Gilbody, both potters, for John Sadler's tile-printing experiment (see essay on *'Printing in Liverpool'*) which states:

'The Town of Liverpool in particular, where the Earthenware manufacture is more extensively carried on than in any other Town in the Kingdom'.[35]

One hundred and thirty-two potters voted in the 1761 parliamentary election and are recorded in *'An alphabetical list of the Free Burgesses who polled'*, published by R. Williamson in the same year. Of these, seventy-seven 'plumped' for Sir William Meredith. This event is commemorated on two examples in the exhibition - a delftware jug (Cat.12) and a porcelain mug (Cat.98).

The second half of the 18th century saw a gradual decline in the pottery industry in Liverpool. In January 1769 at a meeting of the Conversation Club the subject for discussion was *'The Causes of the Decline of the Potters' business in this town and by what means it might be made to flourish'.*[36] The Poll Books also indicate a decrease since only 78 potters are recording as voting in the 1790 election. This downward trend is shown in reverse by the number of retailers appearing in Liverpool directories as 'Staffordshire Merchants'. In 1766 there are none but in 1790 there are 23, doubling to 46 by the end of the century.

Competition with Staffordshire potters, in particular Josiah Wedgwood, and threat from foreign competition are cited as two of the major causes for the decline in the local pottery industry. In 1774 Enfield openly acknowledges Wedgwood's growing popularity:

'ENGLISH porcelain, in imitation of foreign China, has long been manufactured in this town; and formerly not without success. But of late this branch has been much upon the decline, partly because the Leverpool artists have not kept pace in their improvements with some others in the same way ; but chiefly because the Staffordshire ware has, and still continues to have so general a demand, as almost to supersede the use of other English porcelain. The great perfection to which this art, both in works of utility and of ornament and taste, is carried at the modern ETRURIA, under the direction of those igenious artists Messrs. Wedgewood (sic) and Bentley, at the same time that is highly serviceable to the public and reflects great honour upon our country, must be unfavourable to other manufactories of a similar kind'.[37]

The development of the canal system previously mentioned, enabled the safe and easy transit of breakable goods from Staffordshire in contrast to the hazards of transport over rough unsurfaced roads. In addition, the effect of the war with North America, begun in 1775, affected every branch of Liverpool trade. With the signing of peace in 1783, prosperity returned but the local industry had been severely dented. Liverpool merchants turned their attentions away from pottery-making to warehousing and other sources of income. The city centre pothouses closed down, the last being that of Seth Pennington in 1805.

The Herculaneum Pottery, in Toxteth on the banks of the Mersey, established in 1796, managed to continue the potting tradition until 1840. (See essay on *'Herculaneum'*). The history of the firm is excellently documented by Alan Smith,[38] who attributes the eventual closure of the firm to *'changing conditions on Merseyside, in particular the expanding needs of the Mersey Dock and Harbour Board'.*[39]

A small book entitled *'The Commerce of Liverpool'* devotes one chapter to the *'Earthenware Trade'*. Despite being written in 1852, only just over ten years after the closure of the Herculaneum Pottery, there is no mention of the local ceramic industry. Liverpool's importance is as a major centre for the export of pottery, not as a pottery producer:

'The estimated weight and value of earthenware of all sorts manufactured in the United Kingdom are 160,000 tons and £3,500,000 and the majority of our exports are made through Liverpool and London.'[40]

Liverpool's last pottery closed over 150 years ago but as this exhibition shows, the wares *'can be favourably compared with the best products of any other British pottery-making town in those days'.*[41] These surviving pots are a present-day reminder of one of the city's past, and sometimes forgotten, industries - the pottery and porcelain that was once 'Made In Liverpool'.

E. Myra Brown

Footnotes

1 Richard Brooke, *Liverpool as it was, During the last Quarter of the Eighteenth Century, 1775 to 1800,* 1853 p.3

2 Richard Brooke, *op cit* p.16

3 'City' status was conferred on Liverpool by a Royal Charter, granted by Queen Victoria, in 1880.

4 1565 *Liverpool Town Books,* Vol.1 fo.143v (Picton Reference Library) quoted in George Chandler, *Liverpool,* 1957 p.270

5 Michael Stammers, 'Commentary' in Liverpool Packet No.7, *Liverpool Shipping,* published by Scousepress

6 1565 *Liverpool Town Books,* vol.1 fo.144v (Picton Reference Library) quoted in William Enfield, *An Essay Towards the History of Leverpool,* 1774 p.24

7 George McLoughlin, *A Short History of the First Liverpool Infirmary 1749-1824,* 1978 p.1

8 George McLoughlin, *ibid*

9 Richard Brooke, *op cit* p.37

10 George McLoughlin, *op cit* p.2

11 George McLoughlin, *op cit* p.3

12 William Enfield, *op cit* p.24

13 Richard Brooke, *op cit* p.44

14 William Enfield, *op cit* p.38

15 Richard Brooke, *op cit* p.534

16 Richard Brooke, *op cit* p.96

17 George McLoughlin, *op cit* p.6ß

18 Richard Brooke, *op cit* p.233

19 1667–8 *Moore Rental,* fo.71v (Picton Reference Library) quoted in George Chandler, *op cit* p.331

20 William Enfield, *op cit* p.90

21 George Chandler, *op cit* p.285

22 Richard Brooke, *op cit* p.239

23 William Enfield, *op cit* p.7

24 Richard Brooke, *op cit* p.245

25 Richard Brooke, *op cit* p.241

26 William Enfield, *op cit* p.89

27 Knowles Boney, *Liverpool Porcelain of the Eighteenth Century and its Makers,* 1957 p.2

28 Alan Smith, *The Illustrated Guide to Liverpool Herculaneum Pottery,* 1970 p.1

29 Alan Smith, *op cit* pl.3

30 Knowles Boney, *ibid*

31 *The Post Boy,* 23rd May 1710 quoted in Alan Smith, *op cit* p.2

32 Knowles Boney, *op cit* p.4

33 Frank Britton, 'Some Sources of Delfware Clay', E.C.C. *Transactions* Vol.13 pt.1 1987 p.30.

34 *Williamson's Liverpool Advertiser,* 3rd December 1756 quoted in Bernard Watney, *English Blue & White Porcelain of the 18th Century,* 1973 p.69

35 Knowles Boney, *ibid*

36 *Williamson's Liverpool Advertiser,* 27th January 1769 quoted in Knowles Boney, *op cit* p.7

37 William Enfield, *op cit* p.90

38 Alan Smith, *op cit*

39 Alan Smith, *Liverpool Pottery* p.61 (Pub: City of Liverpool Museums)

40 Braithwaite Poole, *The Commerce of Liverpool* 1854 p.41

41 Alan Smith, *op cit* p.4

LIVERPOOL EARTHENWARES AND STONEWARES

Research into the 18th century production of pottery in Liverpool during the past thirty years or so has been advanced by two particular circumstances:- (i) the destruction of parts of the city during the Second World War, and (ii) the road-building demands of modern traffic needs. Both these 'events' have resulted in opportunities to search the ground below pavements, roads and destroyed buildings, to reveal fragments of kiln furniture and manufacturing shards. The resultant finds have provided concrete evidence to support (or destroy) the attempted attributions of earlier collectors and scholars, and the documentary sources explored by writers in the past. The vast amounts of ceramic material which have been fortuitously unearthed have given us *real* evidence of the variety of wares, *earthenwares, stonewares,* and *porcelains,* - which were produced in Liverpool in the 18th century.

Documentary sources have already shown that potting had become established as a Liverpool trade as early as the late 17th century [1] and that up to about twenty-five potteries of one kind or another came into production in the following century. It is fully accepted that delftware was the principal product, but it should not be forgotten that rough earthenwares for the kitchen and tavern were also part of the output, as has been confirmed by the finding of much mottled lead-glazed earthenware such as the jug recovered during the building of St. John's Market [2] - the kind of material which no doubt continued to be produced by the potteries in the surrounding area at Ormskirk, Prescot and St Helens. Although tin-glazed earthenware was, to some extent a luxury article, the thousands of fragments which have been discovered beneath the pavements in areas where potteries were working show that delftware must be considered as Liverpool's most important earthenware product.

Delftware (tin-glazed earthenware), because of its tendency to chip at the edges and because of its poor resistance to thermal shocks, is not a particularly good material for tablewares, for which porcelain is far better suited. However plates appear to have been made in profusion, decorated in cobalt blue with oriental designs (Cat. 7), some of which are also found on porcelain made in Liverpool (Cat. 59). Considering the large quantities of plates decorated in this way which have survived it would appear reasonable to suggest that they were used in upper class and merchant houses as decoration, arranged on dressers, mantlepieces and so forth, as well as having been used for purely utilitarian purposes. That plates, basins, chamber pots, wash bowls and other such basic household pots were made in undecorated delftware seems certain, though hardly any have survived. A plain plate, unearthed by Joseph Mayer over a century ago and several shards discovered in recent years suggest that plain delftwares were made in quantity for everyday use, but it is the decorated material which captures our imagination today in the form of colourful bowls, wall-pockets, mugs, jugs, char-pots, puzzle jugs and so on. The roundel (Cat. 42) from China Plate Farm, Newton-cum-Larton in Wirral, is a fine piece of documentary ware, reminding us of the sadly lost tin-glazed slab '*A West Prospect of Great Crosby 1716*' and the Merchant Taylors' lozenge-shaped tablet

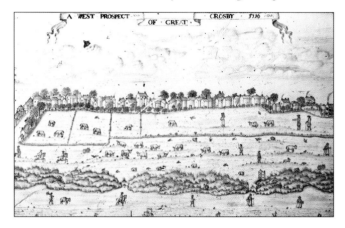

'*A West Prospect of Great Crosby 1716*' Delftware plaque, destroyed in WWII (Mayer Collection).

of 1722, formerly in Crosby Church and later at the Merchant Taylors' School where it was destroyed after the Second World War.[3] The beautiful tin-glazed ship bowls (Cat. 4) made, it is thought, to commemorate the fitting-out of particular vessels, or some other occasion provide magnificent evidence of fine earthenware potting, incorporating oriental motifs with purely western designs.

In the present exhibition an attempt has been made to show matching shards with complete examples (Cat. 20), and from the excavated fragments we can at least recognise the spirit of the designs used even if absolutely exact comparisons cannot always be made.

Of all the tin-glazed ceramic articles made in Liverpool, tiles are amongst the most fascinating, both in their early, hand-painted form, and in the later transfer-printed styles referred to elsewhere. Most were probably made for fireplaces, with polychrome or blue decoration, of vases of flowers or simple figure groups and landscapes, plain ones for the hearth. Some tiles were made for mural decoration of which a single handsome version from a larger panel is shown (Cat. 26). These all, it is felt, owe inspiration to Dutch work of this kind. A few tile fragments which match borders and corners have been unearthed on manufacturing sites and are shown alongside the complete pieces (Cat. 41).

Fragments of kiln furniture, saggars, stilt-pins, shelves etc. which have been found on or near the sites of 18th century Liverpool potteries give us some idea of how the wares were stacked and fired, and in association with unglazed biscuit shards and fragments of completely decorated pottery, provide conclusive evidence of manufacture. Most of these have been found in the area of William Brown Street (formerly Shaw's Brow) and in the Byrom Street, Fontenoy Street area lower down the hill and at the top end of Dale Street.

A considerable quantity of such material is held in the ceramic study collections in Liverpool Museum. A rare find was made in Lord Street on the site of the first documented Liverpool Pottery, the Lord Street Pothouse (1710), where, amongst other things, fragments of a tin-glazed cup were discovered, with its glaze materials still in place but unfired. A biscuited but unglazed bleeding bowl handle was also found, its heart-shaped piercing proving that this style was not confined to Bristol! Finds such as these make it clear that the tin-glaze potters were attempting to supply all aspects of the domestic market for pots, leading us to a type of tin-glazed/salt-glazed pottery, apparently unique to Liverpool, which will be discussed shortly.

The manufacture of salt-glaze is normally thought of as a particularly Staffordshire activity, but while Liverpool was attempting to compete with Staffordshire (especially at the period just before and after the construction of the Trent-Mersey canal, completed in 1777, which brought Staffordshire pots cheaply to the coast for export) there can be little doubt that Liverpool was also working with salt-glaze for heat-resistant table-wares. Excavated evidence has shown this to be the case, as with the salt-glazed stilt rings found in Chorley Court, Dale Street, in 1914[4] and several pieces of plain salt-glazed specimens found alongside other ceramic wasters. From a documentary point of view there are

Saltglazed stoneware stilt rings found in Chorley Court, Dale Street in 1914 by Peter Entwistle.

salt-glazed teapots, and bowls with 'Liver Bird' reliefs, a distinctively Liverpudlian emblem which has been 'proved' to have been used by the Liverpool porcelain potters (Cat. 132), whatever the Staffordshire connoisseurs might think! There is also the firm documentation of a salt-glazed election mug of 1761[5] made to support Sir William Meredith's parliamentary campaign of that year. (Other 1761 pieces in tin-glaze and porcelain were also produced for that event Cat. 12 & 98). Equally important are the porcelain shards in salt-glaze shapes from the Gilbody porcelain site, referred to elsewhere. A tea canister in salt-glaze commemorating one Henry Muskett, fully documented elsewhere [6] also gives evidence of this activity amongst the Liverpool potters (Cat. 50). However much, or little, salt-glazed stoneware was made in Liverpool in the 18th century, there is little doubt that it was produced for a limited period of time, and alongside tin-glazed potting it seems to have produced a curious hybrid type we call tin-glazed/salt-glazed stoneware, or as it has been christened 'delftstone'.

Littler's blue, a well-known Staffordshire salt-glazed type, was made by firing pieces previously dipped in a cobalt slip, in a salt-glaze oven. Simeon Shaw (1829) [7] makes reference, somewhat ambiguously, to *'Coffee and Tea Pots........some glazed with lead ore; and the white, all salt glaze.'* We believe that this refers to the fact that finer salt-glazed wares (tablewares) were sometimes given a thin lead-glaze dip prior to salt-glazing. If this is so would it not be logical for the Liverpool potters, familiar with tin-glaze, to apply a tin-glaze coating to their pots prior to salt-glazing? This, at least, is the conclusion to be reached by examining closely examples of so-called 'delftstone', of which several examples are shown (Cat. 43-48). That this was an experiment to meet competition (a) from the porcelain makers and (b) from the Staffordshire manufacturers seems most likely, though as few pieces survive it was clearly not particularly successful. The present writer examined this problem in much greater detail than is possible here in 1978.[8] and one example has been scientifically tested to show the presence of salt-glaze.

Although tin-glazed earthenware appears to have been made in Liverpool until about the end of the 18th century (especially for apothecary wares), as a common domestic material the end of delftware manufacture must have arrived by about 1775-80. New and improved ceramic materials were coming on the scene, notably creamware and pearlware, both, it is believed, extensively made in Liverpool to compete with the Staffordshire innovators. In the absence of marked pieces, or even clearly attributable excavated fragments, it is extremely difficult to make precise identification of either of these groups. Of the pearlwares there are two pieces in the exhibition (Cat. 51 & 52) which have reasonably firm connections with the town, - a bowl with the 'Liver Bird' inside it, and a jug which refers to the 'Watchmakers', a clear link to a trade particularly associated with Liverpool and its environs.

Generally speaking attempts to identify Liverpool creamwares of the pre-Herculaneum period are also fraught with difficulty, especially as it is well-known that Wedgwood (and perhaps others) were sending blank pieces to Liverpool for transfer-printed decoration, as discussed elsewhere. Guy Green and Richard Abbey,

both specialising in printed decoration must, it is felt, inevitably have been using 'home grown' blanks as well as Staffordshire material, and the presence of the Flint Mug Works,[9] from pre-1772 until the 1790s suggests, by its very name, the manufacture of a product of which a basic material is flint. A number of creamware pieces are of a shape and style which do not suggest a Staffordshire source, and two particular items (Cat. 188 & 217) show how a transfer print on a bowl of 1782 was used later on a Herculaneum tobacco jar of post 1796 date. The very fact that Herculaneum made vast quantities of creamware in its early days points to the continuity of a tradition rather than the implanting of a new one.

The two potteries, Park Lane Pothouse and Flint Mug Works close to the southern end of the town, working in the later 18th century, suggest a gradual migration of the trade from the potbanks in the centre of Liverpool. As the mercantile city grew and wealthy merchants were building their Georgian town houses in terraces which have now, alas, mostly gone, it would be natural for the smoky industrial pothouses to move away, just as surely as the trade itself declined to make way for more profitable enterprises. So until the advent of Herculaneum in 1796 at the extreme southern end of the town, whose wares are much more firmly identifiable, our understanding of the late 18th century creamwares and pearlwares must remain a matter of conjecture. Perhaps later possible discoveries of shards from the Flint Mug Works on Parliament Street will help us out (if they were not all thrown into the river!), but this must wait for future workers to explore. In this context it is extremely important to remember that the

Flint Mug Works advertised, in 1773, *'a large assortment of cream colour or Queensware, manufactured at the said work....'* and in the following year the proprietors Rigg and Peacock advertised *'.....where they intend carrying on the business of making all kinds of cream-coloured earthenware Etc.'* [10]

That some of the older pot banks did survive until the end of the 18th century and into the beginning of the 19th is well-known (e.g. Pennington & Edwards on Shaw's Brow and The Islington China Manufactury), nor must we forget the Canning Street Pottery on Scotland Road (1824-40) which advertised, at its sale in 1840, *'.....comprising workshops for two throwers, five turners, four printers, and suitable conveniences, and workshops for all other branches of the business.'* [11] but this must surely have been manufacturing in a style vastly different from the 18th century potters, and more in the spirit of Herculaneum which will be discussed later.

Alan Smith

Footnotes

1   Joseph Mayer, *The History of the Progress of the Art of Pottery in Liverpool,* 1855

2   Alan Smith, *An Illustrated Guide to Liverpool Herculaneum Pottery,* 1970

3   Joseph Mayer, *ibid*

4   Alan Smith, *op cit* pl.13

5   Joseph Mayer, *ibid*

6   Knowles Boney, 'Documentary Liverpool Saltglaze', *Apollo* Dec. 1960

7   Simeon Shaw, *History of the Staffordshire Potteries,* 1829 p.149

8   Alan Smith, 'An Enamelled, Tin-glazed mug at Temple Newsam House', *Leeds Arts Calendar* No. 82 1978

9   Rose Meldrum, 'Liverpool Creamware; The Okill Pottery', N.C.S. *Newsletter* No. 82 1991

10   *Liverpool Advertiser* 29 October 1773 and 4 February 1774 Quoted in full in Alan Smith, *An Illustrated Guide to Liverpool Herculaneum Pottery,* 1970 pp. 10-11

11   *The Staffordshire Advertiser,* 1840 Quoted in full in Alan Smith *op cit* p.67

LIVERPOOL PORCELAINS – The Early Factories

Identifying the porcelains made in Liverpool during the 18th century has always proved to be a complicated and frustrating affair but has provided a rewarding challenge to those who endeavour to find the answers.

While other towns and cities which made soft paste porcelain in the 18th century (with the exception of London) had only one manufacturer or factory, Liverpool had 8 main manufacturers or partnerships which operated at 7 different sites between 1754-1805 (see map on page 28).

The map shows the locations of the various porcelain producing factories in Liverpool during the 18th century.

Site 1 shows the pothouse on Shaw's Brow (now William Brown Street, where Liverpool Museum is now situated) which was occupied by Samuel Gilbody from about 1754 to 1760. The buildings on the opposite side of the road were used as his decorating establishment and warehouse, from where he advertised his pots for sale.

Site 2, next door to Gilbody's factory, was occupied by Richard Chaffers & Co, Philip Christian, and finally Seth Pennington, in succession from about 1754 to 1805.

Site 3 was the Haymarket Pothouse, where, in 1783, it was advertised that 'English China of fine Quality' was being produced by Zachariah Barnes and James Cotter.

Site 4 pinpoints the factory on Brownlow Hill which was run by William Reid from 1755 until his bankruptcy in 1761. James Pennington took over the factory in 1763, but in 1768 he moved production to Park Lane (**site 5**) where he continued until 1773. No wares have yet been attributed to either of these factories.

John Pennington's factory was at **site 6**, on Copperas Hill, from about 1772 until 1779 when he moved to Folly Lane (**Site 7**). He died in 1786 and production was continued by his wife Jane Pennington until 1794. The site was subsequently taken over by Thomas Wolfe & Co., and will be discussed by Brian Allaker and Trevor Markin later in this section.

Recent archaeological discoveries made by the Museum of London have made it necessary to reattribute two groups of wares - namely those previously ascribed to William Ball and William Reid of Liverpool - to the factories at Vauxhall and Limehouse in London respectively.[1] William Ball himself has been found only to have been a factory manager, not a factory owner as previously thought.[2]

The removal of these two groups of porcelain from the Liverpool camp has cleared the board, as it were, so that the remaining groups of Liverpool porcelain can be viewed more clearly. Hopefully the factories with no wares yet attributed to them may be identified as our knowledge grows.

Map of Liverpool and Toxteth Park showing the sites of the 18th century porcelain factories, and the Herculaneum Pottery.

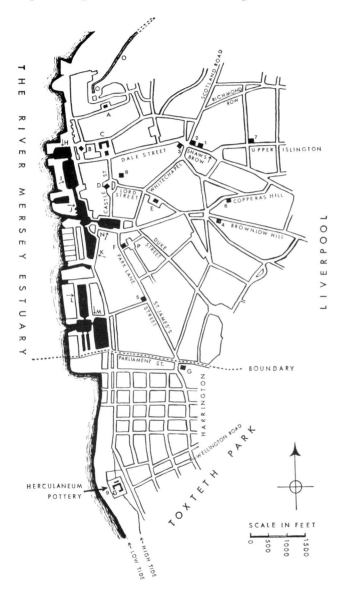

1 SHAW'S BROW POTTERY Samuel Gilbody, the elder and Thomas Morris from 1714-1752; Samuel Gilbody, the younger until c.1760 (production of porcelain from c.1754).

2 SHAW'S BROW POTTERY John Livesley, mortgaged to Richard Chaffers 1747 (production of porcelain from c.1754); Philip Christian 1765-1778; Seth Pennington from Sept. 1778 with John Part until 1799, J. Edmundson 1799-1803, J. Edwards 1803-1805.

3 HAYMARKET POTTERY Leased to John Livesley 1751; Zachariah Barnes and James Cotter (production of porcelain c.1783-1796).

4 BROWNLOW HILL CHINA WORKS Run by William Reid c.1755-1761; James Pennington 1763-1768.

5 PARK LANE POTHOUSE John Eccles & Co.; Robert Thwaites; Robert Willcock; James Pennington (production of porcelain) 1768-1773.

6 COPPERAS HILL POTTERY Thomas and John Mears; John Pennington c.1772-1779.

7 FOLLY LANE (UPPER ISLINGTON) Leased to Thomas Shaw 1743; John Pennington (production of porcelain) from 1779-1786; Jane Pennington until 1794; Thomas Wolfe & Co. from 1795-1800.

8 PRINTED WARE MANUFACTORY, HARRINGTON STREET John Sadler and Guy Green (transfer-printing on pottery from c.1756); Sadler retiring in 1770; Green retiring in 1799.

9 HERCULANEUM POTTERY 1796-1840

A ST. PAUL'S CHURCH
B ST. NICHOLAS' CHURCH
C TOWN HALL AND EXCHANGE FLAGS
D ST. GEORGE'S CHURCH
E ST. PETER'S CHURCH
F ST. THOMAS' CHURCH
G ST. JAMES' CHURCH
H DRY BASIN
I GEORGE'S DOCK
J OLD DRY DOCK
K SALTHOUSE DOCK
L KING'S DOCK
M QUEEN'S DOCK
N OLD DOCK
O LEEDS-LIVERPOOL CANAL
P CLIEVELAND SQUARE

(Courtesy: Alan Smith)

It is most fortunate that we have such a varied and representative selection of Gilbody porcelain in this exhibition. However, it should be stressed that the wares from this factory, which was only in production for about six or seven years, are extremely scarce, particularly examples decorated in underglaze blue. Chemical analysis has shown Gilbody porcelains were made in a phosphatic body containing bone ash.

In 1966 Professor Alan Smith, former Keeper of Applied Art at Liverpool Museum, was fortunate enough to recover many shards relating to the Gilbody factory from road works being carried out in William Brown Street, directly opposite the museum itself. These shards were greatly added to in 1990, when a further chance for recovery - again due to roadworks - presented itself. [3]

Several of these shards can be seen in the exhibition alongside complete examples, such as the coffee can with its elaborate silver-shaped handle (Cat. 60), dish (Cat. 56), and the coffee pot (Cat. 53). Several fragments relating to the bird-like spout and scrolled handle of this piece were found. Interestingly this bird-like spout bears strong similarity to a spout found on a tin-glazed stoneware coffee pot (Cat. 45). The decoration on the Gilbody coffee pot is most unusual, with an oriental landscape on one side and a European scene on the other. All examples of 18th century blue and white porcelain painted with European scenes are very rare. Many pieces in this group were greatly influenced by the shapes used for salt-glazed stoneware such as the coffee pot discussed and the teapot (Cat. 64) with crab-stock handle and spout. The polychrome examples

were tastefully decorated in soft enamel colours which sank into the soft shiny glaze complimenting the white body (Cat. 66-73). Intricately moulded pieces were also produced such as the salt (Cat. 61) standing on a cluster of sea shells and decorated in red and gold, and the creamboat (Cat. 62) moulded in the form of over-lapping leaves. Many shapes follow silver prototypes such as the blue and white sauceboat (Cat. 57) and the mug with its elaborate handle, beautifully painted with English flowers (Cat. 72).

The standard of decoration on some of the Gilbody pieces is amongst the finest seen on English 18th century porcelain. The coffee pot (Cat. 66) displays this with its fine bird decoration. Figures were also made by the factory [4] and several are included such as 'The Sportsman' (Cat. 74) shown with several matching shards which were recovered from the roadworks previously mentioned. Sets of figures depicting the seasons have also been identified. 'Spring' is represented here (Cat. 73) painted in soft enamels.

The porcelains produced by Richard Chaffers and Co. can be divided into two groups: one containing bone ash and another with a soapstone body. The early phosphatic wares containing bone ash appear very grey and hard. The blue and white examples are painted in a dark grey-blue, and single numerals are sometimes found on the bases or inside the footrims (Cat. 81). The small teapot decorated with an oriental landscape and with a most unusual flower knop (Cat. 77), displays some of these features. The shape of the rare salt, (Cat. 76) is taken directly from a silver shape with a moulded gadrooned border, the decoration being a mixture of oriental and English inspiration. The two mugs (Cat. 83 & 84) display the spur handle which is typical of this group. One is painted in underglaze blue, iron-red and gilt, the other finely painted with figures in bright enamel colours which stand out on the grey phosphatic body.

In June 1755 Richard Chaffers and his partner Philip Christian signed an agreement with Robert Podmore who was previously employed by the Worcester Porcelain Co.[5] He was to become their factory manager and to divulge to them the secret ingredient - soapstone - which was used at Worcester. In 1756 Richard Chaffers & Co. took a lease on a soaprock mine in Cornwall and by the end of that year received their first delivery of soapstone.

The pieces made in this soapstone body are visually different to the earlier phosphatic wares. The colour of the glaze varies. On some pieces it is clear, and on others it can be tinted in various degrees of blue.

A group of figures containing soapstone is attributed to Chaffers.[6] They include a large white bust of George II on a shaped plinth, an example of which can be seen in Liverpool Museum; a large figure of Ariadne, reclining; and representations of Milton and Shakespeare.

A white figure of a Nun, which is included in the exhibition (Cat. 108), was taken from a Bow prototype. Also exhibited is a coloured figure of *"La Nourrice"* (Cat. 99) which is a direct copy of a Chelsea figure.

Footrims on bowls, saucers and cups often display a distinctive profile curving inward at the base.

Underglaze blue pieces are painted in a brighter shade of cobalt blue than those in the earlier group. The magnificent coffee pot (Cat. 90) shows the high standard reached by this factory. It is sharply and gracefully potted in a form which flares out towards the base, and is well balanced with its simple strap handle, cover and turned knop. The decoration is restrained, the pattern fitting the shape of the pot well and the tone of the cobalt blue complements the tinted shiny glaze. Another coffee pot of different shape (Cat. 93), again with a plain strap handle, is painted in European style. As previously stated this form of decoration is very rare.

Octagonal moulded teawares were also made by this factory. The 'Jumping Boy' pattern, seen on the tea bowl and saucer (Cat. 92), was copied from the Chinese and was also used by Bow and Gilbody (many Gilbody shards were found displaying this pattern). It can also be found on plain shapes.

Miniature pieces were also produced. A coffee pot with strap handle and a cup (Cat. 97) both painted in blue with an island scene, are included in the exhibition.

Polychrome decoration reached a very high standard at this time and often surpassed that of contemporary Worcester. One jug (Cat. 107) is exquisitely painted with birds and another (Cat. 100) is painted with a portrait of the King of Prussia.

Many unusual shapes were produced such as the cream pail and ladle (Cat. 103), painted with red plants and green leaves, and outlined in grey to give a simple but very eye-catching form of decoration. Figure painting in the oriental style and fine flower painting are also represented.

Overglaze transfer-printing (see essay on *Printing in Liverpool*) was also carried out, as can be seen on the jug (Cat. 87) with its pear-shaped body, printed with a drinking scene and a number of birds and butterflies.

After Richard Chaffers' death in 1765, Philip Christian carried on the porcelain works on Shaw's Brow. Chaffers' widow retained an interest in the factory until 1769 when Christian bought her share of the Company. It was at this time that Christian's son, also named Philip, joined the business as a partner. From then on, they traded under the name Philip Christian and Son.

As Christian merely continued in the manufacture of soapstone porcelain at Shaw's Brow, the style of potting and decoration did not change over-night. It is therefore sometimes difficult to differentiate between late Chaffers and early Christian wares. The blue and white mug (Cat. 114) is a good example of this: it has a strap handle which is usually associated with the products of Chaffers, the base is flat and unglazed (a common feature of Liverpool mugs), but it also has a chamfered edge at the base, a characteristic of Christian wares. The painting is also in a style adopted by Christian - the fisherman with his line is spontaneously painted, and a large number of dots are used to make up the scene. This feature can also be seen on the tea bowl and saucer bearing the date 1766 (Cat. 118).

Footrims on the tea wares became much straighter and sharper, and were usually under-cut on the inside. The black printed mug (Cat. 121) confirms that Christian continued to use the strap handle for a short time, as it is dated 1768.

Large pieces were also made: the guglet (Cat. 115) is most unusual, and is again freely painted with an oriental scene. A magnificent blue ground garniture, perhaps an altar set, can be seen in Liverpool Museum. Blue grounds are represented in the exhibition by the covered vase (Cat. 126), with the panels painted with English flowers.

Moulded wares feature strongly in the Christian group. The sparrow beak jug (Cat. 110) is typical with a profusion of moulded scrolls and leaves and cartouches painted with oriental landscapes. The handle on this jug was also used by Chaffers (Cat. 82) and Seth Pennington (Cat. 137). The spout on the coffee pot (Cat. 123) is also moulded and contrasts with the plain body; the handle, with its comma-shaped terminal, was introduced by Christian, although it must be borne in mind that this moulded handle shape was also used by Seth Pennington after he purchased the factory in 1778.

The blue and white sweetmeat dish and the asparagus server (Cat. 112 & 117) are among the more uncommon products of this factory.

In 1778 the factory on Shaw's Brow occupied by Philip Christian & Son was taken over by Seth Pennington and John Part and continued in production until 1805. They carried on making porcelain using the same moulds as previously used by Philip Christian, but they did not make soapstone porcelain; instead they opted for a bone ash formula. The quality of Seth Pennington's porcelain varied considerably, the earlier wares being quite accomplished, but as time went on the standard deteriorated.

The high 'Chelsea' ewer (Cat. 135) is typical of this group and is painted in enamels with a bird in branches; this shape was also used by Christian. The moulded cup (Cat. 130) and the printed bell-shaped mug (Cat. 133) are displayed with matching shards which were discovered in Liverpool in the 1960s.

Fine moulded pieces were made such as the palm-leaf-column teapot (Cat. 136) (again this shape was first used by Christian) and the sauceboat (Cat. 132), which is moulded with the Liverpool 'Liver birds.'

By the use of dated pieces and excavated material a group of wares has recently been isolated from the Pennington group and reattributed to John and Jane Pennington. [7] A jug with a distinctive handle and mask spout is now accepted as the product of John Pennington (Cat. 139). It bears the date 1772 and therefore cannot be the work of Seth Pennington as he was not in production until 1778.[8] The mask used on this jug is quite different to the Seth Pennington version (Cat. 131). In addition, part of a handle which was excavated on the site of John Pennington's factory at Folly Lane (Upper Islington) is shown together with a coffee pot with a matching handle form (Cat. 154). A coffee cup and can with a small distinctive roll handle (Cat. 144 & 153) are also included from this group.

A number of other pieces, such as the attractive vase and cover, painted in underglaze blue and poly-chrome enamels (Cat. 152), and the teapot inscribed *'Alice Adkinson'* (Cat. 155) have not yet been linked to a factory site and are therefore still attributed with the blanket term of 'Pennington'.

A small group of wares which are marked HP in underglaze blue (Cat. 156 & 157) are tentatively attributed to the Haymarket pothouse which was operated by Zachariah Barnes and James Cotter from c.1783-1796. This factory was situated in what is now the entrance of the Liverpool to Birkenhead tunnel.

There is still ignorance surrounding the making of porcelain at the factory on Brownlow Hill which was run by William Reid from c.1755-1761 and by James Pennington from 1763. In 1768 James Pennington moved to Park Lane where he operated until 1773. It is probable that the wares of these two manufacturers are hidden in one or more of the groups already discussed. It is unlikely that any excavations could be carried out at Park Lane due to disturbance over the years, but it would still be possible to make valuable finds on the Brownlow Hill site. It is therefore hoped that, in the not-too-distant future, some excavations may be carried out at this important site and another layer of mystery which surrounds Liverpool porcelain may be lifted.

Roderick Jellicoe

Footnotes

1   B. Watney, 'Vauxhall China Wares 1751-1754', E.C.C. *Transactions* Vol.13 Pt.3 1989
     English Ceramic Circle and Museum of London, *Limehouse Ware Revealed*, 1993
     John Potter, 'The Search for the Limehouse Pottery', Morley College Ceramic Circle *Bulletin*, Second Series No. 1 Oct. 1992.

2   M. Hillis, 'The Liverpool Porcelains', N.C.S. *Occasional Paper* No.1 1985

3   A. Smith, 'Samuel Gilbody - some recent finds', E.C.C. *Transactions* Vol.8 1971
     M. Hillis & R. Jellicoe, 'Further Finds of Gilbody Porcelain', N.C.S. Journal Vol.8 p.15 1991.

4a   P. Bradshaw, *18th Century English Porcelain Figures 1745-1795,* 1981 pp. 260-3
     D. Delevigne, 'The Shepherd', E.C.C. *Transactions* Vol.8 Pt.1 1971

4b   B. Watney, 'Gilbody Figures 1754-1761 A Short Review', E.C.C. *Transactions* Vol.10 Pt.5 1980

5   B. Watney, *English Blue and White Porcelain of the 18th Century,* 1963 p.69

6   B. Watney, 'The King, the Nun and other figures', E.C.C. *Transactions* Vol.7 Pt.1 1968

7   M. Hillis, 'The Liverpool Porcelain of John and Jane Pennington', N.C.S. *Journal* Vol.6 1987

8   L. & M. Hillis, 'Late Christian or early Pennington?', N.C.S. *Journal* Vol.5 1984

LIVERPOOL PORCELAINS – Thomas Wolfe & Co.

Thomas Wolfe began to manufacture earthenware in 1782 at Stoke upon Trent. In October 1795 he took over the lease on a small porcelain manufactory in Liverpool from Jane (widow of John) Pennington and subsequently formed a partnership with Miles Mason and John Lucock to manufacture porcelain there. The prime purpose of this manufactory at 1-2 Upper Islington (previously called Folly Lane) was to provide Miles Mason with Chinese-type wares for his London retail business at 131 Fenchurch Street after the East India Company ceased the importation of Chinese porcelain (probably due to finding evidence of 'ringing' at one of its auctions by Miles Mason and some other dealers)[1] although Thomas Wolfe probably welcomed the opportunity to learn the art of porcelain manufacture. The other member of the partnership, John Lucock, was an engraver.[2] Thomas Wolfe already had a Staffordshire warehouse at 48 Old Dock, Liverpool [3] so he was well set up to ship porcelain to Miles Mason in London.

The manufactory was small compared with Wolfe's other works in Stoke upon Trent. Fronting onto Upper Islington, it measured 201 feet and the side bordering onto St. Anne Street measured 75 feet. Within this rectangle was contained a single circular biscuit kiln with a smaller kiln beside it, a small circular gloss kiln and a sizeable rectangular straightening kiln. The site had an engine house and a mill for grinding its own material together with the usual dipping, potters' and throwing rooms. Wolfe already had a steam engine of Boulton and Watt type at Stoke and it appears that one of the first things that he did at Islington was to erect a similar steam engine. Very few potters were employing steam engines at this period.

In June 1800 the partnership was dissolved by mutual consent and shortly afterwards Mason began to manufacture porcelain for himself at Lane Delph, Staffordshire. Wolfe used his newly acquired skills to manufacture porcelain at Stoke upon Trent.

In 1968 immediately prior to the site at Islington being bulldozed to make way for a wider road and houses, Alan Smith excavated a sherd tip on the site at the point marked XXX on the plan.[4]

Several hundred sherds were found and are now held in Liverpool Museum. The vast majority are unglazed and about a quarter decorated with underglaze blue prints. There is a small number of glazed sherds including three or four decorated with overglaze enamelling. The wasters mostly consist of fragments of tea bowls and saucers with a smaller number coming from teapots, sugar boxes, creamers and plates. The odd sherd suggests that other wares were manufactured such as tankards and tureens although no extant examples have been recorded. There are no distinctive handle or spout shapes amongst the sherds and only one knop was found. Vertical reeding of various widths, 2-1-2 vertical fluting and spiral fluting were used to vary the shapes.

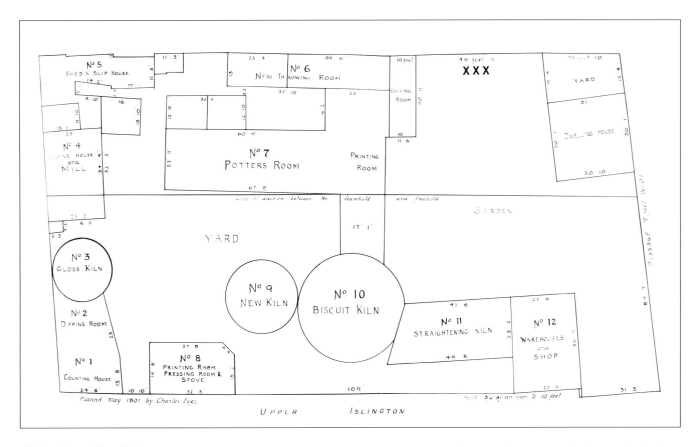

Plannd May 1801 by Charles Eyes

Underglaze Blue Prints

Apart from areas of the prints being washed in by hand, there is no sign of hand-painted designs having been used. A detailed examination of the decorated sherds grouped them into six main designs with the occasional variation such as an alternative border pattern. Most of the sherds are of the 'Shuttered Windows' and 'Dagger Border' designs[5,6] which are by far the most common found on extant wares of this manufactory.

Plan of the Islington China Manufactory, Liverpool, drawn up by Charles Eyes, May 1801. The area in which shards were excavated is marked on the plan 'XXX' (Entwistle Papers, Liverpool Record Office).

Although very few sherds were found of the other four designs the fact that they were mostly at the biscuit stage of production tends to confirm their origin. Very few wares of these four designs have been recorded and most of those are in the exhibition (Cat. 158-163).

Enamelled Patterns

Of the few enamelled sherds found only two are large enough to suggest a pattern. One is part of a spirally fluted saucer showing a floral border and the other decorated with a basket of flowers as used by several manufactures including New Hall (pattern 171). However, the bottom of the basket is different from other versions in having a section clear of colour. Five or six examples of this version have been recorded including the spirally fluted creamer on display which when compared with the plain version is undoubtedly of Wolfe Mason Lucock origin (Cat. 164).

The display of wares by Thomas Wolfe & Co. has been designed to show some of the basic shapes used by the manufactory with matching sherds and, together for the first time, all the known patterns.

Trevor Markin
Brian Allaker

Footnotes

1   G.A. Godden, *Mason's China and the Ironstone Wares*, Antique Collectors Club (Revised Edition 1991)

2   *Staffordshire Pottery Directory*, Hanley 1802

3   *Gores Liverpool Directory*, 1796

4   A. Smith, E.C.C. *Transactions*, Vol.8 Pt.2 1972 p.199

5   T.L. Markin, 'Thomas Wolfe: Tea Wares at Liverpool and Stoke', N.C.S. *Journal* Vol.7 1989

6   B. Allaker, 'John Lucock', N.C.S. *Newsletter* No. 83 1991 (reprint of typographical errors N.C.S. *Newsletter* No.84 1991)

Additional Notes: see also

T.L. Markin, 'Fisherman and Rod Underglaze Blue Pattern', N.C.S. *Newsletter* No. 85 1992

T.L. Markin, 'The Wolfe Mason Lucock Version of the Dagger Border Pattern', N.C.S. *Newsletter* No. 86 1992

T.L. Markin & B. Allaker, 'The Attribution of Factory Z to Thomas Wolfe of Stoke-on-Trent', N.C.S. *Newsletter* No. 88 1992

J.J. Murray, *Thomas Wolfe of Liverpool & Stoke*, Private publication 1980

LIVERPOOL PORCELAINS – Herculaneum Porcelains

My bible was W.B. Honey's '*Old English Porcelain*' first published in 1928. My 1948 edition badly let me down concerning Herculaneum porcelains. I was told *'The productions are usually indistinguishable in style from contemporary Staffordshire wares of little interest to the collector. They are generally marked with the name of the pottery and a liver-bird….'*.

The 1977 revised edition does not add to this (mis-) information but Franklin Barratt certainly deleted Mr Honey's typical dismissal – *'and of little interest to the collector'*. He also correctly added a footnote drawing attention to Professor Alan Smith's E.C.C. paper[1] and his 1970 pioneer work '*The Illustrated Guide to Liverpool Herculaneum Pottery'*[2]

In the foreword to this book, I stated *'The scope and quality of these often unmarked or unfamiliar pieces will, I am sure, pleasantly surprise collectors….'*. I write these present notes without the benefit of seeing the 1993 exhibits but I have every confidence that I could repeat my 1970 thoughts – with even more conviction for over the years our eyes have been awakened to more and more splendid quality porcelains from this still neglected factory.[3] Many of the elegant, well-decorated, vases seem to emulate the fashionable Paris porcelains (Cat. 261) rather than being as Mr Honey stated *'usually indistinguishable in style from contemporary Staffordshire wares'*.

Visitors to this Exhibition will be able to see for themselves the colourful and I believe tasteful array of Herculaneum teawares. Even without the advantage of handling the pieces they can see the wonderful white body beneath that characteristically glossy, almost oil-like, glaze. One can also marvel at the quality of the gilding, the splendid flower-painting and those superb landscapes with added figures. These especially are surely unique to this porcelain factory and serve to show that this non-Staffordshire factory was catering for a very high-class market. It was not concerned with cutting corners, with making wares down to a price. The management may have introduced some bat-printed designs but they seem to be mainly unique designs and most attractive (Cat. 267).

We now have a band of dedicated collectors of Herculaneum wares and our own Bulletin *'The Herculaneum Echo'*.[4] Research should and undoubtedly will continue and be rewarded. It is much needed for really we still know little about the porcelains. We lack even basic information of when porcelain was first introduced at this earthenware-producing factory and when it was discontinued. My early bible stated that the factory *'made porcelain from 1801 until its closing in 1841'*. Was Mr Honey correct? What evidence do we have?

I think he was wrong, certainly about the termination date but I do not know of any evidence. I can only bring to mind one dated example, the small initialled (presentation) teapot inscribed under the base *'Herculanium (sic), Oct 2, 1805'* (Cat. 256). The majority of teawares, the most commonly found articles, seem to fall within the approximate period 1805-1815 but we may still have failed to identify the later productions. Did perhaps the body and glaze change after about 1820? Any variation from the accepted earlier norm would help to throw us off the scent. Perhaps this exhibition or resulting research will throw light on this and other problems. The range of known teaware shapes is also surprisingly small if the production of porcelain really lasted for nearly forty years.

The overriding difficulty is that so few pieces bear a factory mark - Mr Honey was so wrong in stating (if he was referring to porcelain) that they are generally marked with the name of the pottery and a liver-bird. Museums, authors and organisers of exhibitions tend to seek out the marked examples giving a false picture of the real situation. The very few printed-marked pieces known to me are ornamental objects - vases, bulb pots or little ewers and stands (Cat. 265). Do any of the standard teawares or the rarer dessert services bear the printed full name mark with the City crest - the Liver-bird? I think not, although a few examples of an early period bear the impressed HERCULANEUM mark.

An impressed large 'L' initial occurs rarely on the usually wide and glazed-over footrim of the major items in some tea services of the approximate period 1805-15 but why was this easily missed initial mark used when with little trouble a clear publicity name-mark might have been employed to better advantage? According to Mr. Robert Scarlett's research on pattern numbers the Herculaneum porcelain sequence climbs to at least 1415. No tally marks have so far been reported.[5]

My idea of the history and identification of Herculaneum porcelain may in fifty years time prove to be as incorrect as I now consider Mr Honey's brief remarks of the late 1920s. If real progress is to be made they will derive from the staging of exhibitions such as this, where a large assortment of specimens is gathered from a wide range of sources, so presenting a broad picture and stimulating questions from perhaps fresh minds. We certainly need a new, revised and enlarged edition of Alan Smith's 1970 book.[2] I am sure that we would now both acknowledge that the attribution of some of the original illustrations of porcelains is open to question and that the range is by no means now complete or fully representative of the factory's porcelains.

A new book on these mainly nineteenth century Liverpool ceramics is much wanted, it would be a herculean task (!) but so rewarding. In the meantime look closely at this array of typically beautiful, well-produced Herculaneum porcelains.

Geoffrey A. Godden

Footnotes

1   Alan Smith, 'The Herculaneum China & Earthenware Manufactory, Toxteth, Liverpool', E.C.C. *Transactions* Vol.7 Pt.1 1968

2   Alan Smith, *The Illustrated Guide to Liverpool Herculaneum Pottery,* 1970

3   Warrington Museum & Art Gallery, *Herculaneum, The Last Liverpool Pottery,* N.C.S. 1983

4   *The Herculaneum Echo* is a privately published Bulletin for collectors, produced and edited by P. Hyland

5   See Robert Scarlett, *Pattern Numbers on Porcelain and Pottery,* N.C.S. Issue 2 Sept. 1991

PRINTING IN LIVERPOOL

The early history of transfer-printing on ceramics and enamels remains unclear both in the 'inventor' and the method of his invention. The most likely candidate is John Brooks, an engraver apprenticed in Birmingham, who first petitioned for a patent on 10th September 1751 claiming to have:

> 'Found out a method of printing, impressing, and reversing upon enamel and china from engraved, etched and mezzotinto plates and from cuttings on wood and mettle, impressions of History, Portraits, Landskips, Foliages, Coats of Arms, Cyphers, Letters, Decorations and Other Devices.'

This petition was unsuccessful as were his two later applications in January 1754 and April 1755. Perhaps he was not the first and by 1751 transfer-printing by some method was already practised in Birmingham or else-where thus negating his petitions for a patent. If so, no evidence has yet been found.

From Liverpool came a second claim for the invention of transfer-printing. John Sadler, a printer with his assistant Guy Green, on 2nd August 1756 swore an affidavit, as a preliminary to a patent application, that in the space of six hours they had printed twelve hundred tiles of different patterns and that they had been upwards of seven years in finding out the method of printing tiles and making trials and experiments for that purpose. Perhaps the claim of seven years of experiments

was included to pre-date John Brooks' application of 1751. If so, despite the assistance of Charles Brooks, Member of Parliament for Liverpool, Sadler's endeavours to petition for a patent came to nothing and no such application appears to have been lodged. Thus, despite four attempts, no patent was ever granted for transfer-printing however performed.[1] It should be noted that

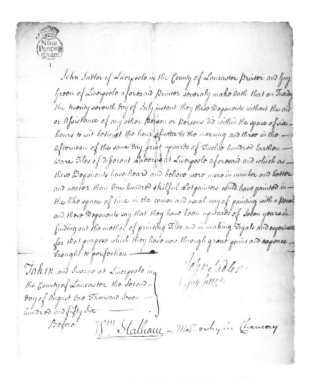

John Sadler and Guy Green's affidavit of 2nd August 1756.

the transfer-printing method of both these early contenders was overglaze and not underglaze, the latter being a somewhat later development.

That John Sadler's method of transfer was by glue bat has been ascertained by Paul Holdway, first suggested by him in 1986 [2] and later confirmed.[3] The tiles used by Sadler and Green for their demonstration and for their first printed wares were of plain white delftware commonly manufactured in Liverpool with prints taken from engraved woodblocks (Cat. 195-198).[4] Although showing a considerable saving in cost over the hand painted English and Dutch tiles which they imitated, these were not popular and within a year they were replaced by transfers from copperplates mostly framed in handsome rococo borders (Cat. 199), although unframed designs were produced, and some enamelled-over tile prints are known (Cat. 203 & 205). Most printing was in black but a very limited range of other colours was obtainable though rarely found.

From this beginning printing on flat delftware tiles, Sadler and Green progressed to printing on white porcelain, both from the Liverpool manufacturers (Cat. 170 & 178), and from Longton Hall and Worcester (Cat. 171 & 179), as well as on hollow delftware (Cat. 187), salt-glaze and enamels (Cat. 172, 174-175). It is not clear whether Sadler & Green employed their own engravers but it would seem most likely. Indeed in a letter to Josiah Wedgwood on 13th August 1763, they reported:

We have got all the sizes of Bute drawn from a mezzotinto painted by Ramsey - they'll do. The Pint is engraved and I expect will be finished by

Wednesday next, and the other will be done as fast as possible, we having the engraver under our Eye.[5]

Richard Abbey was apprenticed to Sadler in 1767 as, it is presumed, an engraver prior to opening his own shop in Liverpool in 1773 where he sold all sorts of Queen's Ware *'printed in the neatest manner'* and in a variety of colours, some signed with his name. Thomas Billinge[6] was probably employed by Sadler from the late 1750s before setting up his own engraving establishment in Liverpool about 1765. His signature appears on two pieces of Liverpool porcelain with engravings of George III (Cat. 178) and William Pitt. A further engraver's name, Jeremiah Evans, [6] also appears on porcelain linked with Sadler in an engraving of the King of Prussia (Cat. 65) and Sadler's name in various forms appears occasionally on both printed tiles and porcelain.

This liberty however was not extended to Sadler and Green when printing on Josiah Wedgwood's creamware. Perhaps spurred on by the hopes of business through the printed likenesses of George III and Queen Charlotte whose coronation in 1761 followed their wedding by a fortnight, Wedgwood concluded an agreement on the following day, 23rd September 1761, with Sadler to print on his new improved creamware, an agreement which ran until at least the death of Wedgwood in 1795. Sadler himself retired in 1770 and the business was taken over by Guy Green until he too retired in 1799.

Whilst at first the sheer quantity of Wedgwood's printed creamware business almost overwhelmed Sadler and Green, after Sadler's retirement this gradually decreased during the 29 years with Guy Green in sole charge. To supplement his declining business it appears likely that Green undertook printing on his own behalf on bought-in plain creamware. This view is supported by the appearance of the same instantly recognisable prints on a variety of different creamware bodies, some unmarked and others impressed marked by different potters.[7]

It is not known with certainty what happened to the copperplates on Green's retirement although evidence does suggest that at least those not out-dated by later events were taken over by the Herculaneum factory and continued in use for some years.

Printing undertaken by the Liverpool Herculaneum Pottery, established in 1796,[8] continued in the tradition of overglaze black or bat printing with their own most competent engravers including George Martin of Toxteth whose fine stipple engraving of Nelson is shown on a creamware jug (Cat. 224).

The Herculaneum factory also developed an extensive export trade with the United States. Wares printed over glaze with portraits and patriotic scenes designed specifically for the American market had been exported before Herculaneum was founded, but, alas, these wares are unmarked and thus cannot be positively attributed to Liverpool manufacturers. However, the advent of Herculaneum saw a considerable increase in this Anglo-American printed pottery. The volume of this trade is not really reflected in this exhibition. As can be imagined American museums have many fine marked Herculaneum export wares, those of the Smithsonian

Institution in Washington, the Peabody Museum in Salem, the Mattatuck Museum and the Boston Museum of Fine Arts being outstanding. Alan Smith illustrates a goodly number of such splendid jugs, mugs and plates in his Herculaneum book.[8,9]

The underglaze blue hot press printing process, started at Worcester, was continued at Caughley and from there reached Staffordshire by about 1784 [10] where it was adapted for use on earthenware as well as porcelain. The Liverpool porcelain manufacturers were well acquainted with underglaze blue printing as can be seen in the many fine examples in the exhibition.

The Herculaneum factory was also responsible for a good, well-transfered range of underglaze blue-printed earthenwares. Indeed the *'Liverpool Albion'* of July 9th 1827 gives a full eye-witness account of the printing room at the Herculaneum factory which graphically describes both methods of printing. [11]

The final overglaze printer that must be included is that elusive 'Liverpudlian' Joseph Johnson. Included in some ten or more overglaze prints on creamware are the signatures 'J. Johnson - Liverpool' and 'Joseph Johnson - Liverpool' (Cat. 180-181,216), or variations of these, with one print dated 1789 and others including the signatures of the Liverpool engravers Richard Walker and Richard Abbey. From this it would appear to be a simple matter of consulting Liverpool trade directories to track down the man and his business. Alan Smith in his book [8] gives the meagre results of his extensive search for Johnson whose name does not appear in any Liverpool trade directory. He concluded, without any certainty, that Joseph Johnson was likely to have been a native of Ormskirk working as a decorator on the outskirts of Liverpool in the Ormskirk area until his death in 1805.

As can be seen, the early and later years of 'Printing in Liverpool' are well researched and clearly defined. However much remains hidden of the over-glaze printing and potting activities in and around Liverpool during the last quarter of the 18th century offering considerable scope for further pleasurable research.

David Drakard

Footnotes

1   E. Stanley Price, *John Sadler, A Liverpool Pottery Printer*, 1948

2   Paul Holdway, 'Techniques of Transfer Printing on Cream Coloured Earthenware', N.C.S. *Creamware and Pearlware Exhibition Catalogue* 1986

3   David Drakard, *Printed English Pottery - History and Humour in the Reign of George III 1760 - 1820*, 1992

4   Anthony Ray, 'English Printed Tiles', E.C.C. *Transactions* Vol.9 Pt.1 1973
     Anthony Ray, *English Delftware Tiles*, 1973

5   For further details on the relationship with Wedgwood see E.N. Stretton, 'Early Sadler Prints on Wedgwood Creamware', *Proceedings of the Wedgwood Society* No.8 1970

6   Norman Stretton, 'Two Liverpool Engravers : Jeremiah Evans and Thomas Billinge', *Antique Collecting* Oct. 1983

7   David Drakard, *op.cit* pp 51-3

8   Alan Smith, *The Illustrated Guide to Liverpool Herculaneum Pottery*, 1970

9   Robert H. McCauley, *Liverpool Transfer Designs on Anglo-American Pottery*, 1942.
     This rare book is still the standard work on these wares.

10.   David Drakard and Paul Holdway, *Spode Printed Ware*, 1983

11.   Colin Wyman, 'The Early Techniques of Transfer Printing', E.C.C. *Transactions* Vol.10 Pt.4 1980

HERCULANEUM

When Josiah Wedgwood coined the name 'Etruria' for his new manufactory in 1769 he only used it for the building and place, but when Worthington, Humble and Holland adopted the name 'Herculaneum' they applied it not only to their new works at Toxteth but they also put it on their products. There is a subtle difference, for Wedgwood was a skilled potter himself from a long established potting family, experienced in the craft as well as being a good businessman, whereas Worthington, Humble and Holland were simply investors and proprietors who knew nothing of the technical side of potting but who did realise the value of a good 'trade mark' in marketing terms. Wedgwood very rarely indeed stamped 'Etruria' on his pots, but used his own name; our Herculaneum entrepreneurs used their chosen factory name itself, at least on those pots which were retailed from their own Liverpool warehouse though probably not on those distributed by speculators and middlemen. In marked contrast to the activities of the older Liverpool potters of the 18th century who advertised only in local newspapers, Herculaneum was clearly part of the 'modern' commercial world, where the value of a good trade name was recognised in a potentially expanding market of international importance.

The foundation of Herculaneum in 1796 was also quite different from the small family business of the early Liverpool potters. In addition to using some of the older skilled workmen of the locality, the proprietors of

Herculaneum started by bringing in about *'forty hands, men, women and children'* from Staffordshire [1] (perhaps about 50 people to work in the factory), and by 1806 they invited investment by advertising 50 shares at £500 each, realising a working capital of some £25,000, a vast sum of money in those days. By 1827 there were over 300 workpeople at the pottery according to a contemporary account by a reporter from the *'Liverpool Albion'* of that year, [2] and views of the establishment with rows of bottle ovens, workshops, a windmill and an adjacent dock as illustrated give us some idea of the

Detail from a share certificate showing an engraving of the *'Herculaneum China & Earthenware Manufactory'*

extensive scale of the enterprise. Two further points should be made relative to the setting up of the *Herculaneum China & Earthenware Manufactory* (see details elsewhere[3]); one is that the proprietors chose buildings on the River Mersey with a dock suitable for bringing in materials and exporting finished goods; the second concerns the workforce, for here we have a mass-movement of people from one part of the country to another (which was common in 19th century industry), creating, as it were, an isolated fragment of Staffordshire on the banks of the Mersey, speaking their own dialect, worshipping in their own chapel (Methodist) and working on a mass-production basis to a scale hitherto unknown in the Liverpool area.

There can be little doubt that Herculaneum flourished for the first twenty-five years or so of its life, and did so by taking advantage of its site. Staffordshire, in spite of the economies brought about by the Mersey/Trent canal, still had to transport raw materials and finished goods over long distances, thereby increasing its costs. Herculaneum, on the other hand, was on the coast itself, and took advantage of this situation especially in its exploitation of overseas markets in Europe and particularly North America. When its decline did set in it was due not to adverse competition from Staffordshire (though this cannot have helped in the economic depression of the post-Napoleonic era), but was brought about mainly by the shift of interest of investors in the Liverpool area, and a consequent loss of energy and efficiency at the works itself by about 1830. Dock construction, shipbuilding, engineering and other such maritime/mercantile/ industrial interests were becoming far more profitable than pot-making on the

Mersey waterfront, and although business continued, on a reduced scale and under new management from 1833, the end was in sight, leading to final closure in 1840.

The Herculaneum factory produced the entire range of ceramic products being made in Staffordshire in its day, from creamwares in its early years, mocha and slip-coloured creamware, porcelain, stonewares, blue-printed earthenwares, moulded and later printed ware, lustreware and virtually everything else in fashion. Most of these groups are shown in the exhibition and all, except the early creamwares which continue a Liverpool tradition, follow a Staffordshire parentage. Although most of the decoration was achieved by enamelling, under and overglaze printing and under-glaze painting in the factory, a number of outworkers were employed on the decorating side (e.g. William Dixon (Cat. 262), William Lovatt) and it is more than likely that some designing and modelling was done by outside artists (e.g. William Bullock (Cat. 250), Solomon Gibson), [4] while some of the relief moulds for stonewares might have been bought from specialist mould-makers in Staffordshire. In addition there is evidence that the factory sometimes 'bought in' blanks from elsewhere for internal decorating (Cat. 222); on the trading side it is known that the products of many Staffordshire firms were retailed through Herculaneum's own warehouse in Duke Street. [5] So although Herculaneum was to some extent isolated, it was not independent but relied quite heavily on business contacts and co-operation with its Staffordshire neighbours.

Until about 1815 creamware was, perhaps, the main product of the Herculaneum factory, mostly decorated with transfer prints (Cat. 215) and sometimes with hand-enamelling, sometimes both in combination (Cat. 217).

The range of prints used is bewilderingly large, inspiration for these coming from contemporary prints, armorial bearings, maritime subjects, agricultural subjects, military and naval heroes, classical sources, political figures, literary verses and mottoes, floral decorations, trophies of arms and so forth. Particular mention must be made of the large and handsome jug entirely covered with prints which has become almost a 'catalogue' for identifying other Herculaneum creamwares (Cat. 224). Although the jug itself is unmarked, research has shown it to be undoubtedly Herculaneum; the stipple-print of Nelson below the lip is signed *'G. Martin sculpt.'*, George Martin being listed in the registers of St Michael's Church, Toxteth, as 'pottery engraver'. The enormous number of prints made for the American market can only be seen in American museums and private collections, though one is shown here which did not 'get away' (Cat. 182). American subjects, featuring George Washington (especially immediately following his death in 1799), political cartoons, views, ships and American emblems were all made for this lucrative market, at least until 1808 when an embargo on trade with the United States brought this commerce to an end. That American trade was resumed (albeit on a reduced scale) after 1814 is accepted, and the exhibition shows a rare later moulded plate decorated in the 'gaudy Dutch' style favoured by Pennsylvanian immigrants (Cat. 238). The quality of potting and enamelling on some pieces (Cat. 223) can stand comparison with anything done anywhere else.

The same general statement may be made about Herculaneum stonewares, of which some splendid examples are shown (Cat. 245-255). Although in many ways resembling the products of Spode, Turner, Adams etc. from Staffordshire, there are some characteristics which appear unique to our factory. Jugs of ovoid section, for example, do not appear to have been made elsewhere (Cat. 246), nor does the marbled slip-casting in some of these jugs (Cat. 249) occur from other factories. It is impossible to say whether or not all the relief decorations were modelled for, or at Herculaneum, but many appear to be unique to the factory; it must be remembered that relief moulds were available to the potting trade from specialist mould-makers at this time. Some pieces, such as the teapot (Cat. 247) can stand comparison, in terms of elegance of form and quality of finish, with the best made anywhere else, and the same can be said for the fine black basalt jug (Cat. 253). Some modelled busts of contemporary heroes (Washington, Nelson, Napoleon, Admiral de Winter and several others) were produced in stoneware (Cat. 245 & 252), while others, from the same moulds, were done in enamelled earthenware.

Since the publication of my book in 1970 many more Herculaneum pieces have come to light (as it should be), especially in the field of porcelain. This material would seem to have been produced from the earliest days of the factory - at least from about 1800 - and the range of styles of shape and decoration is now known to be far greater than was appreciated over twenty years ago. For this reason an account of Herculaneum porcelain has been added by Dr Geoffrey Godden whose expertise and knowledge in the field of 19th century porcelains is unrivalled (see essay on *Liverpool Porcelains*).

Blue-printed earthenwares formed a very large part of the Herculaneum output from its early years, and many examples are shown. As with the use of moulded reliefs mentioned above, it is sometimes hard to know whether or not some of the engraved plates for printing were 'imported' for use at the factory, but many appear to be unique to Herculaneum. The subjects include English landscapes and town views (Cat. 225 & 226),

'The Duke's Dock, & Warehouses, Liverpool' from 'Lancashire Illustrated', 1832 Drawn by Harwood, engraved by Higham.

willow–pattern variations, floral compositions, orientally-inspired scenes (Cat. 230) and one splendid rendering of the town of Liverpool (Cat. 227). The local views such as this were continued, mostly in black printing (but sometimes blue or sepia) during the closing years of the factory's life, when the establishment had declined in size. These were taken from a book called *Lancashire Illustrated*, published in London in 1832. As designs for parts of large dinner services these prints are of the highest quality (Cat. 241-244), though the pieces

to which they were applied belong to a heavy moulded style, with gadrooned edges, which herald the coming of the Victorian era. Other plates and tablewares of the early 1830s are decorated with prints of sporting scenes, other town views and designs with such exotic names as 'Louvre' and 'French scenery'.

No exhibition such as this, taking in the totality of Liverpool ceramics, can fully represent the wide range of products from Herculaneum, such as was done at Warrington Museum in 1983,[6] when about 150 examples were shown. Nevertheless, the splendid examples illustrated here in the context of the pottery and porcelain of Liverpool, indicate the high level of achievement attained by this, the last of the Liverpool potteries.

Alan Smith

Footnotes

1   Joseph Mayer, *The History of the Progress of the Art of Pottery in Liverpool*, 1855
     It is not quite clear whether Mayer means 'forty potters with their wives and children' or' a total of forty people comprising men, women and children'.

2   *The Liverpool Albion*, July 9th 1827
     The only known copy of this is in the British Museum, all the Liverpool copies having been destroyed in the Second World War.

     See Alan Smith, *The Illustrated Guide to Liverpool Herculaneum Pottery*, 1970 pp.98-107 for a complete transcript.

3   Alan Smith, *The Illustrated Guide to Liverpool Herculaneum Pottery*, 1970 Chapters 2 & 3

4   *op cit* p.32

5   *op cit* pp.55, 56

6   Warrington Museum & Art Gallery, *Herculaneum - The Last Liverpool Pottery* 27 August – 28 September 1983 (N.C.S. Catalogue)

SELECT BIBLIOGRAPHY

This general bibliography – largely compiled by Prof. Alan Smith – does not attempt to list every published source on Liverpool pottery and porcelain. It is however, reasonably comprehensive in its coverage of the articles published by the Northern Ceramic Society and the English Ceramic Circle.

The footnote references following each individual essay should also be consulted as they contain details of many books and articles not included in this select bibliography.

General Books

Edwin Atlee Barber	*Anglo-American Pottery*, 1899
Knowles Boney	*Liverpool Porcelain of the 18th Century and its makers*, 1957
Peter Bradshaw	*18th Century English Porcelain Figures 1745 -1795*, 1981 & 1992
Frank Britton	*English Delftware in the Bristol Collection*, 1982
R.J. Charleston (Ed)	*English Porcelain 1745 - 1850*, 1965
John & Margaret Cushion	*A Collectors History of British Porcelain*, 1992
Peter Entwistle	*The Entwistle Papers* (unpublished – Liverpool Public Record Office) 1939
F.H. Garner & M. Archer	*English Delftware*, 1972
Charles T. Gatty	*The Liverpool Potteries*, 1882
Geoffrey A. Godden	*Eighteenth Century English Porcelain*, 1985
Maurice Hillis	'The Liverpool Porcelains' N.C.S. *Occasional Paper* No.1 1985
Jonathan Horne	*English Tin-glazed Tiles*, 1989
H. Boswell Lancaster	*Liverpool and her Potters*, 1936
Robert H. McCauley	*Liverpool Transfer Designs on Anglo-American Pottery*, 1942
Joseph Mayer	*The History of the Progress of the Art of Pottery in Liverpool*, 1855 & 1871
E. Stanley Price	*John Sadler, A Liverpool Pottery Printer*, 1948
Anthony Ray	*English Delftware Pottery* in the Warren Collection, Ashmolean Museum, Oxford, 1968
Anthony Ray	*English Delftware Tiles*, 1973
Alan Smith	*The Illustrated Guide to Liverpool Herculaneum Pottery*, 1970
Warrington Museum & Art Gallery	*Herculaneum – The Last Liverpool Pottery*, 1983
Bernard Watney	*English Blue & White Porcelain of the 18th Century*, 1973

Articles

Northern Ceramic Society Newsletter

No. 10	item 13	David C. Herbert, 'The United States Frigate Constitution Jug'	1974
No. 16	item 3	Angela Cox, 'Samuel Gilbody in York'	1975
No. 24	item 4	Elizabeth Adams, 'Potteries of the Northwest -Whitehaven, Lancaster and Liverpool'	1977
No. 34	item 2	Alan Smith, 'Liverpool Creamware' (lecture)	1979
No. 39	item 7	Lyn & Maurice Hillis, 'HP Marked Porcelain'	1980
No. 41	item 11	Reginald Haggar, 'Liverpool Porcelain, Fact, Fantasy and Fiction'	1981
No. 43	item 4	John T. Murray, 'William Ball's Liverpool China Works'	1981
No. 43	item 7	Robert Stones, 'Liverpool 18th Century Creamware and Stoneware'	1981
No. 45	item 5	Esmé Lloyd, 'The Country Potteries of St. Helens and Prescot'	1982
No. 51	item 11	Dr & Mrs Rakow, 'Rare Gothic Herculaneum Mark'	1983
No. 52	item 12	Lecture Meeting, 'The Earthenwares and Porcelain of Herculaneum'	1983
No. 56	item 2	Nancy Gunson, 'Herculaneum Supplement'	1984
No. 57	item 14	Gwen & Stan Jenkins, 'Liverpool Pottery and the Tall Ships'	1985
No. 58	item 12	Tony Lonton, 'Another Herculaneum Link'	1985
No. 59	item 3	Lionel Burman, 'More about the Sutton Heath Pottery'	1985
No. 73	item 9	R. Parkin, 'A Herculaneum Teapot'	1989
No. 74	page 37	Geoffrey Godden, 'A Herculaneum Sugar Bowl and Cover'	1989
No. 81	page 46	Anthony Thomas, 'Stories of Ancient Liverpool'	1991
No. 82	page 4	Rose Meldrum, 'Liverpool Creamware: The Okill Pottery'	1991
No. 83	page 33	Brian Allaker, 'John Lucock'	1991
No. 85	page 35	Norman Stretton, 'J. Dixon-Copper Plate Engraver'	1992
No. 86	page 19	Trevor Markin, 'The Wolfe-Mason-Lucock version of the dagger border and related patterns'	1992
No. 87	page 37	Brian Allaker, 'The Traveller and the Duck Pattern'	1992

Northern Ceramic Society Journal

Vol. 1	page 5	Elizabeth Adams, 'Towards a more complete History of the Liverpool China Manufactory'	1972–3
Vol. 4	page 69	John J. Murray, 'The Potting Penningtons of Liverpool'	1980–81
Vol. 5	page 23	Lyn & Maurice Hillis, 'A Liverpool Potter in Trouble, and the Election of 1761'	1984
Vol. 5	page 29	Lyn & Maurice Hillis, 'Late Christian or early Pennington?'	1984
Vol. 6	page 1	Maurice Hillis, 'The Liverpool Porcelains of John and Jane Pennington c.1771–1794'	1987
Vol. 7	page 1	Trevor L. Markin, 'Teawares at Liverpool and Stoke'	1989
Vol. 8	page 15	Maurice Hillis and Roderick Jellicoe, 'Further Finds of Gilbody Porcelain'	1991

English Ceramic Circle Transactions

No. II		p.27	(English Porcelain Circle)	
			B. Rackham & W.B. Honey, 'Liverpool Porcelain'	1929
Vol. 4	Pt.1	p.7	Knowles T. Boney, 'Liverpool porcelain'	1957
Vol. 4	Pt.5	p.13	Bernard Watney, 'Four Groups of Porcelain: Possibly Liverpool. Parts 1 & 2'	1959
Vol. 5	Pt.1	p.42	Bernard Watney, 'Four Groups of Porcelain: Possibly Liverpool. Parts 3 & 4'	1960
Vol. 5	Pt.2	p.67	F.H. Garner, 'Liverpool Delftware'	1961
Vol. 5	Pt.5	p.269	Bernard Watney, 'The Porcelain of Chaffers, Christian and Pennington'	1964
Vol. 7	Pt.1	p.16	Alan Smith, 'The Herculaneum China and Earthenware Manufactory, Toxteth, Liverpool'	1968
Vol. 7	Pt.1	p.48	Bernard Watney, 'The King, The Nun and Other Figures'	1968
Vol. 7	Pt.2	p.100	Alan Smith & Bernard Watney, 'Samuel Gilbody-Some recent finds at Liverpool'	1969
Vol. 8	Pt.2	p.199	Alan Smith, 'Thomas Wolfe, Miles Mason and John Lucock at the Islington China Manufactory, Upper Islington, Liverpool'	1972
Vol. 9	Pt.1	p.36	Anthony Ray, 'Liverpool Printed Tiles'	1973
Vol. 9	Pt.2	p.190	Anthony Ray, 'Liverpool Printed Tiles; some further notes'	1974
Vol.10	Pt.3	p.174	Mrs D.W. Bridges, 'Sadler Tiles in Colonial America'	1978
Vol.10	Pt.4	p.187	Colin Wyman, 'The Early Techniques of Transfer-printing'	1980
Vol.10	Pt.5	p.346	Bernard Watney, 'Gilbody Figures 1754 - 1761: A Short Review'	1980
Vol.11	Pt.1	p.36	Norman Stretton, 'Some unrecorded Liverpool Printed Tiles'	1981
Vol.13	Pt.1	p.63	John Murray, 'More about William Reid; His Family & Factory'	1987
Vol.13	Pt.3	p.200	John H. Harrop, 'The 'Longton' Jug : James Pennington of Liverpool, Wirksworth and Worcester'	1989
Vol.14	Pt.3	p.249	Bernard M. Watney, 'James Giles and Liverpool Porcelain'	1992

Other Articles

Maurice Hillis	'Reid & Ball of Liverpool', *Ceramics* 1 1985
Maurice Hillis	'Elegant Interlopers', *Collectors' Guide* Feb. 1988
Maurice Hillis	'Diversity Discovered', *Collectors' Guide* Aug. 1988
Maurice Hillis	'Whatever Happened to William Ball?' *Collectors' Guide* Jan. 1989
Maurice Hillis	'The Liverpool Mainstream', *Collectors' Guide* Apr. 1989
Maurice Hillis	'In Search of Later Liverpool', *Collectors' Guide* Nov. 1989

CATALOGUE

1 BOTTLE

Tin-glazed earthenware
Liverpool c.1760

h. 9¹/₁₆ in (230mm)
Spherical shape tapering to narrow neck
with cupped rim. In-glaze painted with
floral sprays and Chinese fence in
colours. Glazed base with footrim.

2 PLATE

Tin-glazed earthenware
Liverpool c.1760

d. 9⅝ in (237mm)
In-glaze painted in polychrome with
'Fazackerley' flowers with a spray in the
centre and with four single buds with
leaves around the rim. The reverse
glazed but undecorated.

3 PUZZLE JUG

Tin-glazed earthenware
Liverpool c.1750

h. 7¼ in (185mm)
The bowl of spherical shape with a
cylindrical neck pierced with three
flower-heads of oval and heart-shaped
petals. Three spouts at the rim. In-glaze
painted in blue with dashes around the
rim and down the handle, the belly with
a rhyme flanked by floral sprays.
Inscribed in cursive script, *'Gentlemen
come try your skill / I'll hold a wager if you
will / that you don't drink this Liquor all /
Without you spill or let some fall'*. Glazed
base with partially glazed footrim.

4 SHIP BOWL

Tin-glazed earthenware
Liverpool 1763

d. 9⅜ in (237mm)

The interior, in-glaze painted mainly in blue with touches of red, showing a three-masted fully-rigged ship, inscribed in blue in bold script, *'Sucæss to the Hope, 1763'*. Decorated with floral sprays in blue on the inside rim and around the exterior. Footrim to base.

5 PILL BOX AND COVER

Tin-glazed earthenware
Liverpool c.1760

d. 2 ⁹⁄₁₆ in (65mm)

The squat, circular body in-glaze painted in blue on the underside with a departing ship inscribed *'the Gray Frigate'*, the interior further inscribed *'Cap:t Dundry'*. The cover painted with a stylised flower-head.

6 VASE

Tin-glazed earthenware
Liverpool c.1750-60

h. 8¾ in (222mm)

Baluster-form, in-glaze painted in blue with an oriental scene depicting a palm-tree, house and fence and with two birds in the foreground. Slightly concave base, glazed in the centre. Cover lacking.

7 PLATE

Tin-glazed earthenware
Liverpool c.1750-70

d. 9¼ in (235mm)
In-glaze painted in blue with a chinoiserie landscape depicting a willow tree sprouting from a 'cannonball' tower of rock beside two buildings and, in the foreground, a fisherman in a boat. A trellis border pattern around the inside rim. The reverse glazed but undecorated.

8 WALL POCKET

Tin-glazed earthenware
Liverpool c.1760

h. 7½in (190mm)
Curved cornucopia shape. Press-moulded with a raised design of birds and flowers with slight spiral fluting, and with a shell motif in the centre of the rim. The whole in-glaze painted in polychrome.

9 FLOWER BRICK

Tin-glazed earthenware
Liverpool c.1760

l. 5in (127mm)
Casket-shaped brick on four feet. The feet may originally have been of pedestal shape but have been ground down at some time. The top perforated with six small holes either side a group of nine holes, the central one being larger. The inside is divided into three compartments by two partitions. In-glaze painted in blue with landscapes and buildings on either side, and a bird and sprig at each end.

10 BOWL

Tin-glazed earthenware
Liverpool c.1750

d. 7⅞in (200mm)
Painted in-glaze decoration of the dragon and flaming pearls pattern in inky-blue on the interior and exterior. Raised footrim to base.

11 TEAPOT AND COVER

Tin-glazed earthenware
Liverpool c.1755-65

h. 3⅜in (86mm)
Globular-shaped teapot having a flat cover with flower knop. Blue painted in-glaze decoration of a chinoiserie land-scape around the exterior and a blue wash on the crabstock handle and spout. Narrow footrim, the base glazed in the centre.

12 JUG

Tin-glazed earthenware
Liverpool 1761

h. 4⅝in (118mm)
Baluster-shape with a slightly concave, glazed base and grooved loop handle. The exterior in-glaze painted in blue with an inscription in bold script *'Success to Sir William Meredith / And all his Plumpers Elizabeth Ormes 1761'.* (see also Cat. 98)

13 PUNCH BOWL

Tin-glazed earthenware
Liverpool 1770

d. 10 ³/₈ in (263mm)
In-glaze painted in polychrome, the
exterior decorated with 'Fazackerley'
flowers, the interior with a naive
ploughing scene in blue, manganese,
green and brown. Painted blue inscription
in bold script *Drive on Brave Boys the
Seasons now / God Bless your Work and
Speed the plow / S ★ D. 1770'.*
Polychrome border pattern around
inside rim. Footrim to base.

14 COFFEE CUP

Tin-glazed earthenware
Liverpool c.1750-60

h. 2 ³/₈ in (60mm)
Inverted bell-shape on a low foot, with
loop handle. In-glaze painted in
polychrome with a landscape depicting a
haystack, birds and 'layered' tree,
outlined in manganese. Footrim to base,
glazed in centre.

15 CREAM JUG

Tin-glazed earthenware
Liverpool c.1760

h. 3 ³/₈ in (85mm)
Of pear-shape on a low foot, with a loop
handle. In-glaze painted in polychrome
with 'Fazackerley' flowers and a diaper
border pattern below the rim. Footrim
to base, glazed in centre.

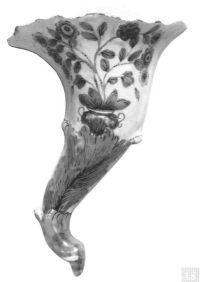

16 JUG

Tin-glazed earthenware
Liverpool 1757

h. 7 5/8 in (194mm)
Pear-shaped with solid spreading foot
and having a ribbed handle with scroll
terminal. Painted in-glaze decoration of
floral sprays in green, yellow and iron-
red. Painted in manganese with the
inscription '*C / R ★ I*' and date '*1757*'.
Flat base, glazed in the centre.

17 FLOWER BRICK

Tin-glazed earthenware
Liverpool c.1760

l. 5 3/8 in (137mm)
A rectangular brick, the top perforated
with eleven small holes on each side of
the central aperture. In-glaze decorated
in polychrome with 'Fazackerley' flowers
on all four sides. The perforations outlined in manganese. The base glazed.

18 WALL POCKET

Tin-glazed earthenware
Liverpool c.1760

h. 8 7/8 in (225mm)
Of curved cornucopia shape, the front
moulded with a raised design of a vase
with flowers emerging from leaves. The
whole in-glaze painted in polychrome.

19 PLATE
Tin-glazed earthenware
Liverpool c.1750-60

d. 8¾in (222mm)
Blue painted in-glaze decoration, the
central design depicting two cockerels
beside a flowering tree within a band of
alternating diaper pattern and debased
Chinese scrolls. The rim decorated with
four floral sprigs surrounded by a border
of alternating lattice pattern and 'feathered'
twigs. The edge of the rim showing traces
of iron-red. The reverse with two fine
blue bands, one in the centre of the base,
the other around the rim. Three stilt pin
marks show clearly on the reverse of the
rim.

20 PLATE, FRAGMENT
Tin-glazed earthenware
Liverpool c.1750-60

d. 11¾ in (300mm)
Blue in-glaze painted in finely 'pencilled'
style with a coat of arms in the centre,
surrounded by a band of alternating
diaper pattern and twig motifs. The rim
decorated with four flowering branches
alternating with a twisted bird and with
a fine band around the inside rim. The
edge of the rim banded in orange-red.
The reverse with four herbal sprigs. The
fragment, probably from a small bowl,
decorated with a chinoiserie pattern
incorporating a twisted bird. The fragment
was recovered from William Brown
Street, Liverpool in February 1972.

21 PLATE

Tin-glazed earthenware
Liverpool 1750

d. 8¾ in (222mm)
The centre in-glaze painted in blue with
bamboo and peonies sprouting from a
hollow rock. The rim decorated with a
diaper pattern alternating with reserves
of debased Chinese scroll symbols. The
centre of the reverse inscribed in cursive
script in blue *'Timothy Hoyle of / Stublee
in Rochdale / Parish / 1750'*.

22 WALL POCKET

Tin-glazed earthenware
Liverpool c.1760-70

h. 7⅞ in (20mm)
Moulded in the shape of a fish, in-glaze
painted in polychrome.

23 PLATE

Tin-glazed earthenware
Probably Liverpool c.1750-70

d. 8½ in (216mm)
In-glaze painted in blue, iron-red,
manganese, yellow and green. The centre
decorated with flowers and foliage in a
vase, the rim with blue leaf sprays
surrounded by a lattice border pattern in
red and blue.

24 DRY MUSTARD POT
Tin-glazed earthenware
Probably Liverpool c.1740-60

h. 2½in (64mm)
Of globular shape having a loop handle with out-turned lower terminal. Decorated with a chinoiserie scene depicting a pagoda, a fisherman in a boat and a twisted rock or tree. The handle decorated with a series of four dots. The decoration painted in blue, iron-red and yellow. The rim showing traces of iron-red. Footrim to base, glazed in the centre.

25 PLATE
Tin-glazed earthenware
Liverpool c.1750-75

d. 8⅝in (220mm)
In-glaze painted in blue with a rural scene depicting two shepherds, one playing a pipe. The edge banded in brown. The design possibly copied from a Nicolaes Berchem etching or engraving.
(see E.C.C. *Transactions* Vol.5 Pt.2 Pl.69)

26 TILE
Tin-glazed earthenware
Liverpool c.1760

h. 4¹⁵⁄₁₆in (126mm)
In-glaze painted in polychrome with a bird on a branch. Originally from a pair of large tile panels.

27 TILE
Tin-glazed earthenware
Probably Liverpool c.1750-75

l. 5in (128mm)
In-glaze painted in dark blue, the centre of the octagonal panel with a river scene with figures in boats. The central design surrounded by a 'cherub' border.

28 TILE
Tin-glazed earthenware
Possibly Liverpool c.1760-70

l. 4⅞in (123mm)
In-glaze painted in manganese with a chinoiserie figure in the centre surrounded by a bianco-sopra-bianco border.

29 TILE
Tin-glazed earthenware
Probably Liverpool c.1725-50

l. 5in (128mm)
In-glaze painted in blue with a house and gates within an octagonal cartouche. The central panel surrounded by a powdered blue border with 'dandelion' corners.

30 TILE

Tin-glazed earthenware
Probably Liverpool c.1750–80

l. 4⅞in (123mm)
In-glaze painted in blue with a octagonal panel depicting a man with a staff. The whole surrounded by a 'Louis XV' border with 'buttercup corners'.

31 TILE

Tin-glazed earthenware
Liverpool c.1755–75

l. 4⁵⁄₁₆ in (125mm)
In-glaze painted in polychrome depicting a scene with a pedlar and a girl.

32 TILE

Tin-glazed earthenware
Probably Liverpool c.1750–70

l. 4¹⁵⁄₁₆ in (125mm)
In-glaze painted in blue with flowers in a vase flanked by birds within an octagonal panel, surrounded by a powdered blue border with 'ragged flower' corners.

33 TILE

Tin-glazed earthenware
Probably Liverpool c.1750–75

l. 5in (127mm)
In-glaze painted in polychrome with an oriental figure surrounded by a 'fish roe' border with 'Michaelmas daisy' corners.

30

31

32

33

34

35

34 TILE

Tin-glazed earthenware
Liverpool c.1750-75

l. 5in (128mm)
In-glaze painted in manganese with a
seated woman, known as the 'Singing
Shepherdess'. The design copied from
a set of etchings by Nicolaes Berchem.
(see Anthony Ray, *English Delftware
Tiles* p.148 Fig.41)

35 TILE

Tin-glazed earthenware
Probably Liverpool c.1750-80

l.4^{15}/$_{16}$ in (126mm)
In-glaze painted in blue with a scene
with a boat and two swans, surrounded
by a 'Louis XV' border with diaper
corners.

36

37

36 TILE

Tin-glazed earthenware
Liverpool c.1760-75

l. 5in (127mm)
In-glaze painted in polychrome with
flowers in a bowl.

37 TILE

Tin-glazed earthenware
Liverpool c.1750-70

l. 5in (128mm)
In-glaze painted in blue with a floral
motif in the centre surrounded by a
running flower and scroll border.

38 TILE

Tin-glazed earthenware
Liverpool c.1750-70

l. 5in (127mm)
In-glaze painted in blue with a scene depicting a man in a boat, surrounded by an 'octagonal dash' border.

39 TILE

Tin-glazed earthenware
Probably Liverpool c.1760-75

l. 4^{15}/$_{16}$ in (126mm)
In-glaze painted in polychrome with a stylised bird, possibly a pheasant, surrounded by a 'trellis' border.

40 TILE

Tin-glazed earthenware
Liverpool c.1740-70

l. 4^{15}/$_{16}$ in (126mm)
In-glaze painted in blue with an ornamental design depicting flowers in a vase, a shaped cartouche and two birds.

41 TILE FRAGMENTS

Tin-glazed earthenware
Liverpool c.1750-80

Max. l. 3in (76mm)
Six tile fragments, five in-glaze painted in blue, one in manganese, decorated with various designs. The fragments were recovered during the re-building of Liverpool Museum and from roadworks in William Brown Street, Liverpool in the 1960s.

38

39

40

41

42 TILE PLAQUE

Tin-glazed earthenware
Liverpool 1753

d. 20⅞ in (530mm)
Documentary plaque of circular shape.
In-glaze painted in blue and manganese
with the arms of Johnson impaling Anton,
inscribed *'I / T E / 1753'* surrounded
by a shell border pattern. The plaque
was originally let into the wall of a
house, known as China Plate Farm, in
Newton-cum-Larton, West Kirby. This
house is believed to have been built by
Ellen (née Anton) and Thomas Johnson
for themselves. Johnson later became
Mayor of Liverpool in the 1760s.

43 COFFEE CAN

Tin-glazed stoneware
Liverpool c.1760-70

h. 2½ in (63mm)
Cylindrical shape with strap handle.
Decorated in the porcelain manner with
a floral bouquet of roses and other flowers,
painted in polychrome enamels.

44 TEAPOT AND COVER

Tin-glazed stoneware
Liverpool c.1760

h. 4¾ in (120mm)
Of globular shape having a plain loop
handle with out-turned lower terminal.
In-glaze painted in blue with floral
sprays. The cover with an onion shaped
knop.

45 COFFEE POT

Tin-glazed stoneware
Liverpool c.1760

h. 6¼ in (160mm)
Of pear-shape on a splayed foot having grooved strap handle with up-turned lower terminal. The moulded spout with bird's head opening and moulded acanthus leaf. Both sides decorated in blue with a panel of flowers in a vase.

46 COFFEE CUP

Tin-glazed stoneware
Liverpool c.1760

h. 2⅝ in (67mm)
Slightly waisted cylindrical shape of light-coloured stoneware. In-glaze painted in blue with a stylised pine tree. The handle lacking but having the remains of an out-turned lower terminal. Narrow footrim to base.

47 COFFEE CUP

Tin-glazed stoneware
Liverpool c.1760

h. 2½ in (64mm)
Of cylindrical shape, slightly flared at rim, on a small raised foot. The handle with a central rib and an out-turned lower terminal. Light-coloured stoneware, in-glaze painted in blue with a river scene depicting a house, an arch and a figure in a boat. Narrow footrim to base, glazed in the centre.

48

50

48 CREAM JUG

Tin-glazed stoneware
Liverpool c.1760

h. 2½in (64mm)
Pear-shaped with silver-shaped rim,
having a loop handle with out-turned
lower terminal. Blue painted in-glaze
decoration of a chinoiserie scene with
house, rock and willow tree. Border
pattern below rim.

49 PUNCH BOWL

Salt-glazed stoneware
Possibly Liverpool c.1760-70

d. 10⅜in (263mm)
A punch bowl, underglaze blue painted
in the porcelain manner with chinoiserie
landscapes around the exterior. The
interior with a broad band of lattice
pattern around the rim and with a border
pattern in the centre, which has run
during the firing. The whole piece having
warped considerably in the kiln.
'MF' monogram painted in underglaze
blue on the base.

50 TEA CANISTER

Salt-glazed stoneware
Liverpool 1760

h. 4½in (108mm)
Slab-built tea canister of square section
with cylindrical neck. Incised decoration
filled with cobalt blue including the
inscription 'Henrey / Muskit / 1760 L'
and 'Elizabeth / Cannon / 1760 / liverp.'

49

51 PUNCH BOWL

Pearlware
Probably Liverpool c.1780–1800

d. 11⅛ in (282mm)
Underglaze blue painted with a 'Liver bird' in the centre of the interior, surrounded by a band of husk pattern. A broad scallop and banded border pattern around the inside rim. The exterior decorated with chinoiserie landscape scenes with pagodas, rocks and willow trees. Deep footrim to base.

52 JUG

Pearlware
Probably Liverpool 1793

h. 8⅛ in (207mm)
Jug of ovoid shape having a cylindrical neck with lip and a moulded double-scroll handle. Underglaze painted in blue with the inscription *'Richard & Martha / HUNT / Another Jug & then / Success to the / Watchmakers / 1793'*, flanked by two scenes with buildings and trees. The neck decorated with a running-leaf border pattern and with two banded lines around the rim exterior. The handle decorated with a feather motif.

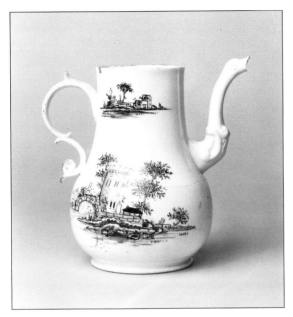

53 COFFEE POT, FRAGMENTS
Porcelain
Samuel Gilbody, Liverpool c.1754-60

h. 6⅞ in (175mm)
Of pear shape on a low foot with a moulded rococo spout with bird's head opening and a leaf-moulded scroll handle. Footrim to base. Cover lacking. Underglaze painted in blue, one side with chinoiserie scenes of pagodas and trees on a rocky island. The other side with European landscapes depicting a castle or turret and bridge beside a river. The cobalt blue painting on both sides has misfired. The three fragments, from a matching spout and handle, were recovered during roadworks in William Brown Street, Liverpool in 1990.

54 COFFEE CAN
Porcelain
Samuel Gilbody, Liverpool c.1754-60

h. 2½ in (64mm)
Of slightly tapering cylindrical form with fluting. Fretted scroll handle. Shallow footrim to base. Underglaze blue painted, the exterior with a flowering branch, two small sprigs and a border pattern around the rim. The rim interior with two banded lines.

55 TEA BOWL AND SAUCER
Porcelain
Samuel Gilbody, Liverpool c.1754-60

d. saucer 4⅞in (124mm)
Painted in underglaze blue with flowers
and foliage sprouting from a hollow
rock. Border pattern of diagonal hatching
interspersed with floral motifs. Narrow
footrim to base.

56 DISH, FRAGMENT
Porcelain
Samuel Gilbody, Liverpool c.1754-60

d. 7⅝in (193mm)
Shallow dish having a fluted rim with
scalloped edge. Painted in underglaze
blue with a willow tree, hollow rock and
peony pattern. Footrim to base. The
unglazed fragment, recovered from
William Brown Street, Liverpool in
1990, is decorated with the same design.

57 SAUCEBOAT, FRAGMENT
Porcelain
Samuel Gilbody, Liverpool c.1754-60

l. 5⅞in (150mm)
Of silver-shape on an oval foot with an
elaborately moulded double-scroll handle.
Underglaze blue painted decoration
depicting a chinoiserie scene with pagodas,
trees and rocky boulders on each side
and a small motif below the lip. The
interior with four stylised floral motifs.
The cobalt blue having run slightly in
the firing, particularly on the inside. The
fragment, decorated with the same
pattern, is from the rim of a sauceboat
and was recovered from William Brown
Street, Liverpool in 1990.

55

56

57

58

58 TEA BOWL, FRAGMENT
Porcelain
Samuel Gilbody, Liverpool c.1754-60

d. 3⅛ in (80mm)
Painted in underglaze blue with a
stylised rock, willow tree and pagoda,
and with two men in a boat on the
reverse. The centre of the interior with
four dots. Footrim to base. The matching
fragment, decorated with the same pattern,
was recovered from William Brown
Street, Liverpool during roadworks in
1990.

59 PLATE
Porcelain
Samuel Gilbody, Liverpool c.1754-60

d. 9⅛ in (232mm)
Underglaze blue painted in the delftware
manner, the well of the plate with a
chinoiserie scene depicting two birds
beside a Chinese fence, hollow rock,
flowers and foliage, and in the distance a
rocky island with pagodas. The rim,
with silver-shaped edge, decorated with
four cartouches of flowers and bamboo,
alternating with a winged insect. Three
under-rim markings of herbal sprigs on
the reverse. Footrim to base. Underglaze
blue painted '8' on base.

59

60 COFFEE CAN, FRAGMENTS
Porcelain
Samuel Gilbody, Liverpool c.1754–60

h. 2¼ in (57mm)

Slightly waisted shape with scroll handle. Painted in underglaze blue with bamboo and peony pattern. The two fragments, decorated with the same design, were recovered from William Brown Street, Liverpool during roadworks in 1990. Both fragments show signs of having misfired.

61 SALT
Porcelain
Samuel Gilbody, Liverpool c.1754–60

l. 4⁵⁄₁₆ in (110mm)

Shell-moulded form on raised shell-encrusted foot. Painted in iron-red enamel and gilding, the centre of the interior with flowering branches and with a border pattern around the rim. The rim exterior decorated with scroll-work flanked by Chinese scrolls.

62 CREAM BOAT
Porcelain
Samuel Gilbody, Liverpool c.1754–60

l. 4⁵⁄₁₆ in (110mm)

Leaf-moulded form with crabstock handle. Painted in iron-red enamel and gilding with a flowering branch sprouting from a rock, flanked by a swan on each side.

63 COFFEE CUP

Porcelain

Samuel Gilbody, Liverpool c.1754–60

h. 2⅜ in (61mm)
Painted in iron-red enamel with a chinoiserie scene depicting two figures, one holding a parasol, the other fishing. Broad footrim to base. Plain loop handle.

64 TEAPOT AND COVER, COVER FRAGMENT

Porcelain
Samuel Gilbody, Liverpool c.1754–60

h. 4¾ in (121mm)
Of globular shape with moulded crab-stock handle and spout. Overglaze painted in iron-red enamel and gilding with a flowering branch, hollow rock and fence design. The slightly domed cover with pointed button knop, also decorated in iron-red and gilding. Shallow footrim. The fragment of a cover, painted in underglaze blue, was recovered during roadworks in William Brown Street, Liverpool in 1990.

65 MUG

Porcelain
Samuel Gilbody, Liverpool c.1757–60
Printed by John Sadler, Liverpool.

h. 5in (126mm)
Of slightly waisted cylindrical shape, having a strap handle with scroll terminal. Faint transfer-printed decoration in black of a portrait inscribed *'KING of PRUSSIA / Elector of Brandenbourg'*, signed *'Sadler Livpl Enl'* and *'Evans. Sc.'*. Two smaller prints either side of the central one. The base with narrow unglazed footrim.

66 COFFEE POT AND COVER
Porcelain
Samuel Gilbody, Liverpool c.1754-60

h. 9¾ in (246mm)
Of elongated pear-shape, having a slender spout and moulded handle with thumb-rest and scroll terminal. Overglaze painted in polychrome enamels with exotic birds and foliage. The interior unglazed. Shallow footrim to base.

67 TEAPOT AND COVER
Porcelain
Samuel Gilbody, Liverpool c.1754-60

h. 4⅝ in (117mm)
Globular shape with roll handle and plain spout. Unglazed interior. The slightly domed cover with pointed button knop. Decorated with a hollow rock, fence and flowering branch pattern, painted in polychrome enamels. Shallow footrim, unglazed base.

68 SPOON TRAY
Porcelain
Samuel Gilbody, Liverpool c.1754-60

l. 5⁵⁄₁₆ in (135mm)
Of lobed shape with flat glazed base. The centre painted in polychrome enamels with a design of flowering branches, bowl and Chinese scrolls, the rim with six small floral sprigs.

69

69 COFFEE CAN
Porcelain
Samuel Gilbody, Liverpool c.1754–60

h. 2½ in (64mm)
Straight–sided with plain loop handle
and flat unglazed base. Painted in polychrome enamels with a scene showing
two aquatic birds beside hollow rocks
and flowering branches.

70 JUG
Porcelain
Samuel Gilbody, Liverpool c.1754–60

h. 9¹⁄₁₆ in (230mm)
Baluster form with slightly up-turned
lip. The moulded handle with thumb-
rest and scroll terminal. Decorated in
polychrome enamels with a chinoiserie
scene depicting a Chinese junk
approaching an island dotted with pagodas,
two swans in the foreground. The
reverse with a three masted ship flying
the British flag, viewed from the starboard quarter. Broad footrim to base.

70

71

71 MUG
Porcelain
Samuel Gilbody, Liverpool c.1754–60

h. 4³⁄₈ in (110mm)
Cylindrical form with flat base and plain
loop handle. Enamel painted in polychrome with two chinoiserie scenes, one
depicting a 'stag hunt'. Both scenes set
within lobed cartouches edged in iron-
red, reserved against a 'bianco-sopra-
bianco' ground of floral motifs and
scrollwork in white enamel.

72 MUG

Porcelain

Samuel Gilbody, Liverpool c.1754-60

h. 3⁹/₁₆ in (90mm)

Of slightly tapering cylindrical shape with flat base and moulded handle with thumb-rest and scroll terminal. Painted in polychrome enamels with a floral spray including back-to-back roses and three smaller floral sprigs. Flat, partially glazed base.

73 FIGURE: A PUTTO BEARING FLOWERS

Porcelain

Samuel Gilbody, Liverpool c.1754-60

h. 4¹/₂ in (114mm)

Slip-cast figure of a putto, emblematic of 'Spring', from a set of 'The Four Seasons', probably after Meissen's set of Putti as Seasons.

(see E.C.C. *Transactions* Vol.10 Pt.5 p.346) This example is glazed and enamel painted in pink, yellow, brown, green and red with some gilding. The figure leans backwards towards his left, supported by a tree-stump. The flat base has a small cylindrical vent, a number of small fire-cracks, one of which opens into a second aperture. A complete set of Putti as 'The Four Seasons' can be seen at Plymouth Museum and Art Gallery.

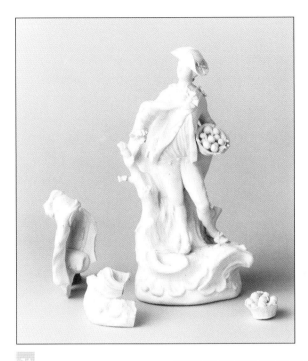

74 FIGURE: 'THE SPORTS-MAN', FRAGMENTS

Porcelain
Samuel Gilbody, Liverpool c.1754-60

h. 9in (229mm)
Slip-cast figure, known as the 'Sportsman' or 'Shepherd', glazed and in the white. The figure wears a jacket and a flowing cloak attached at the front with a rosette, a satchel slung across the body, a hat with turned-back brim and knee breeches. In the left hand he carries a basket of fruit. The figure is supported by a tree-stump and stands on a rococo scroll base which lacks the models of the sheep and small dog. The flat underside is unglazed and has a small vent in the centre. The three fragments; part of the cloak and satchel, a portion of the rococo base and the basket of fruit, were recovered from William Brown Street, Liverpool during roadworks in 1966.

75 PAIR OF FIGURES: TURK AND LEVANTINE LADY

Porcelain
Samuel Gilbody, Liverpool c.1754-60

h. Turk 8¼in (210mm),
h. Lady 7⅝in (195mm)
Both figures slip-cast, glazed and in the white. The Turk, wearing a turban, jacket, trousers, cloak and shoes, stands with his left hand behind his back and with his right resting on his knife, which is tucked into his sash. The companion model wears a head-dress, a long robe

divided at the front to reveal an under-skirt, a short-sleeved cloak, a jewelled belt and slippers. Together the figures give the feeling of movement, as if dancing. These figures were probably copied from Meissen originals. In 1748 Kandler modelled the Turk and Lady in his set of 'Six Orientals'. Staffordshire versions are also known and copies were made c.1756 at Longton Hall.
(see E.C.C. *Transactions* Vol.10 Pt.5 p.346)

76 SALT
Porcelain (phosphatic)
Richard Chaffers, Liverpool c.1754-58

l. 3 1/2 in (89mm)
Of moulded silver-shape with gadrooned border around rim and base. Blue under-glaze painted with a chinoiserie scene on each side, depicting a 'scrolled' rock and sprouting willow tree. Small floral motif at each end and a border pattern and winged insect in the well of the dish.

77 TEAPOT AND COVER
Porcelain (phosphatic)
Richard Chaffers, Liverpool c.1754-58

h. 4 1/2 in (114mm)
Of tapering globular shape with ribbed handle and faceted spout. The flat cover surmounted by a flower knop. Footrim to base. Decorated in painted underglaze blue with a chinoiserie scene on each side and on the cover, and with a border pattern below the outside rim and around the edge of the cover.

78 CREAM JUG

Porcelain (phosphatic)
Richard Chaffers, Liverpool c.1754-58

h. 3³/₈ in (86mm)
Moulded jug of faceted pear-shape with leaf-moulded lip and scroll handle with thumb-rest. Painted in underglaze blue with two panels of stylised flowers flanked by two panels of diaper pattern, four scroll motifs beside the handle terminals and fine outlining.

79 COFFEE CUP

Porcelain (phosphatic)
Richards Chaffers, Liverpool c.1754-58

h. 2¹/₄ in (57mm)
Of slightly waisted, faceted form with scalloped rim and with moulded angular handle. Underglaze blue painted with stylised floral motifs around the exterior, and with fine blue banding on the inside and outside rim. Footrim to base.

80 BOWL

Porcelain (phosphatic)
Richard Chaffers, Liverpool c.1754-58

d. 7¹/₂ in (190mm)
The exterior painted in underglaze blue with a chinoiserie scene with figures. The rim interior decorated with a border pattern of scrolls and diaper patterns. Footrim to base.

81 JUG

Porcelain (phosphatic)
Richard Chaffers, Liverpool c.1754–58

h.10 7/8 in (277mm)

Baluster-shaped jug with moulded lip.
The moulded handle with thumb-rest
and scroll terminals. Decorated in underglaze blue with a Chinese vase of flowers
on one side and a peony spray spreading
around the other side. Blue painted
'comma' terminals on either side of the
handle with a flower and leaf spray running
down the handle. The blue painting has
run slightly during the firing, especially
by the handle. Glazed base with
unglazed footrim.
Marked with a blue underglaze painted
'7' on the inside of the footrim.

82 CREAM JUG

Porcelain (phosphatic)
Richard Chaffers, Liverpool c.1754–58

h. 3 1/8 in (80mm)

Baluster-shape with silver-shaped rim
and with a moulded scroll handle.
Underglaze blue painted decoration
depicting a chinoiserie scene with pagoda
and rock. Diaper border pattern around rim.

83 MUG

Porcelain (phosphatic)
Richard Chaffers, Liverpool c.1754–58

h. 2 3/4 in (73mm)

Barrel-shape, having a moulded handle
with thumb-rest. Painted decoration

of stylised flowers, hollow rock and Chinese fence, in underglaze blue and overglaze red enamel with gilt outlining. Border of alternating diaper pattern and floral motif below outside rim. Shallow footrim to base.

84 MUG

Porcelain (phosphatic)
Richard Chaffers, Liverpool c.1754–58

h. 6⅜in (163mm)
Of barrel-shape having a moulded handle with thumb-rest and knop terminal. Decorated in polychrome with overglaze enamels depicting a chinoiserie scene; a girl with an exotic bird perched on her hand and in the background, a pagoda and rocky island. Painted 'comma' terminals either side of the handle and scroll motifs running down the handle in iron-red enamel. Glazed base with unglazed footrim.

85 COFFEE CAN

Porcelain (phosphatic)
Richard Chaffers, Liverpool c.1754–58

h. 2½in (63mm)
Cylindrical shape with plain loop handle. Overglaze painted in polychrome enamels depicting a chinoiserie scene with a figure beside a table with two vases. Flat base with chamfered edge.

86 COFFEE CUP

Porcelain (phosphatic)
Richard Chaffers, Liverpool c.1754–58

h. 2⁷/₈ in (73mm)
Larger-sized coffee cup of cylindrical
shape tapering to narrow foot. Moulded
angular handle. Overglaze painted in
enamels with a peony and rock design
and two winged insects in purple, green,
iron-red, black and white. Footrim to base.

87 JUG

Porcelain
Richard Chaffers, Liverpool c.1758–60
Printed by John Sadler

h. 7¹/₂ in (188 mm)
Of pear-shape on a spreading foot and
with a high up-turned lip and strap handle
of ear shape. Overglaze transfer-printed
in black with a drinking scene in the
centre surrounded by additional prints of
birds, insects and floral bouquets.

88 TUREEN, COVER AND STAND

Porcelain
Richard Chaffers, Liverpool c.1760–65
Printed by John Sadler

l. 8¹/₂ in (216mm)
Moulded tureen and cover of lobed
shape, the stand of oval shape with a
fluted and indented rim. Overglaze
transfer-printed in black with exotic
birds, four on the dish and cover, one
large print on the stand. Moulded fruit
and leaf knop to the cover. Shaped
footrim to the base of the tureen and an
oval one to the stand.

89 SPOON TRAY
Porcelain
Richard Chaffers, Liverpool c.1760-65

l. 5½in (140mm)
Of fluted shape, underglaze blue painted with a chinoiserie scene depicting 'two men on an island' and with a basket-weave border pattern around the inside rim. Flat base.

90 COFFEE POT AND COVER
Porcelain
Richard Chaffers, Liverpool c.1760

h. 8¾in (223mm)
Of lighthouse form with a flared base and having a strap handle with out-turned lower terminal. The domed cover with flange and topped by a button knop with cone-shaped finial. Underglaze blue painted with a chinoiserie design of a flowering branch sprouting from a stylised rock.

91 MUG
Porcelain
Richard Chaffers, Liverpool c.1760-65

h. 6¼in (160mm)
Of inverted bell-shape on a rounded foot and with a strap handle. Painted in underglaze blue with a peony, bamboo and hollow rock design around the exterior and with a diaper pattern below the rim. Shallow footrim to base.

92 TEA BOWL AND SAUCER
Porcelain
Richard Chaffers, Liverpool c.1758-60

d. saucer 4¹⁄₄ in (108mm)
Octagonal shape, underglaze painted in
blue with the 'Jumping Boy' pattern,
and with an alternating border of diaper
pattern and stylised leaves around the
inside rim. Both painted with mock
Chinese character marks on the base in
underglaze blue.

93 COFFEE POT
Porcelain
Richard Chaffers, Liverpool c.1760

h. 7¹⁄₄ in (184mm)
Of pear-shape on a splayed foot with
plain spout and strap handle. Painted in
underglaze blue with two European
landscape scenes with tall trees, one on
each side. Footrim to base. The cover
lacking.

94 TEA BOWL AND SAUCER
Porcelain
Richard Chaffers, Liverpool c.1760-62

d. saucer 4³⁄₄ in (120mm),
d. tea bowl 3in (77mm)
Painted blue underglaze decoration of
peony, willow tree and Chinese fence
pattern. Footrim to both.

92

93

94

95 TEA BOWL

Porcelain
Richard Chaffers, Liverpool c.1760

d. 3in (77mm)
Painted in underglaze blue with a
stylised rock, willow tree and pagoda
pattern and with a man in a boat on the
reverse. Diaper border pattern around
the inside rim. Footrim to base.

96 CREAM JUG

Porcelain
Richard Chaffers, Liverpool c.1760

h. 3¾in (95mm)
Baluster-shape on a splayed foot, having
a silver-shaped rim and moulded double-
scroll handle. Decorated in painted
underglaze blue with the 'Jumping Boy'
pattern, consisting of two chinoiserie
figures beside a willow tree and twisted
rock or tree. Footrim to base.

97 MINIATURE COFFEE POT AND COVER, COFFEE CUP

Porcelain
Richard Chaffers, Liverpool c.1762-65

h. coffee pot 4½in (115mm)
The coffee pot of pear-shape on a
spreading foot and having a flattened
loop handle and plain, curved spout.
The domed cover with flange and pointed
ball knop. The straight-sided cup curving
in to the foot and with a strap handle.
Both underglaze blue painted with scenes
of trees and rocky islands.

98 MUG

Porcelain

Richard Chaffers, Liverpool 1761

h. 3⁷⁄₁₆in (87mm)

Of straight-sided form, very slightly flared out to foot and with a flat unglazed base. The flat loop handle with out-turned lower terminal. Painted in underglaze blue with the inscription *'Success to / Sir William's Plumpers / 982'*.

This mug commemorates Sir William Meredith's election as one of Liverpool's two Members of Parliament in April 1761. Meredith was a Whig and stood against the sitting members backed by the Corporation. His supporters secured 982 single votes or 'plumpers' for him.

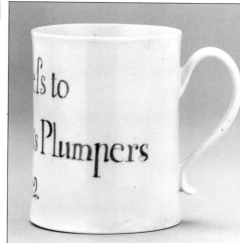

99 FIGURE: 'LA NOURRICE'

Porcelain

Richard Chaffers, Liverpool c.1758-60

h. 5⁷⁄₈in (150mm)

An enamelled model of a nurse wearing a puce head-scarf, blouse with red collar, purplish-blue bodice and yellow shoes. The figure is seated and is breast-feeding a baby wrapped in swaddling clothes. The underside is perforated by a small cylindrical ventilation hole. The Arabic numeral *'2'* incised on the base.

This is one of a small group of figures attributed to Richard Chaffers' factory by Dr. Bernard Watney in 1968. 'La Nourrice' was presumably copied from one of the popular Chelsea models rather than from a French original.

(see: E.C.C. *Transactions* Vol. 7 Pt.2 p.48)

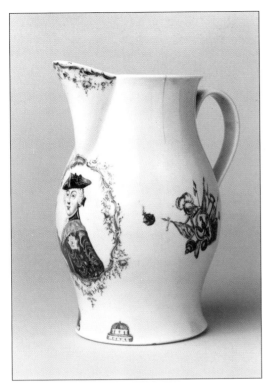

100 JUG
Porcelain
Richard Chaffers, Liverpool c.1760

h. 7 1/2 in (190mm)
Of baluster-form having a strap handle with a flattened up-turned terminal. Overglaze painted in polychrome enamels with a portrait of the King of Prussia within a cartouche of purple scrolls and garlands, above two crowns on ermine stands. The portrait flanked on either side by trophies of war including a smoking grenade. The interior decorated with a Prussian eagle on the base, trophies of war on the lip and scattered with floral sprigs. The base glazed with unglazed footrim.

101 COFFEE CUP
Porcelain
Richard Chaffers, Liverpool c.1758-60

h. 2 3/8 in (61mm)
Of cylindrical shape tapering to narrow foot with plain loop handle. Overglaze painted in iron-red enamel and gilding; the exterior with a bird amongst flowers and foliage, the interior with a bud and line border around the rim. Footrim to base.

102 TEAPOT AND COVER

Porcelain

Richard Chaffers, Liverpool c.1760–65

h. 5 ¾ in (146mm)

Of globular shape with plain spout and roll handle. The slightly domed cover with pointed ball knop. The exterior painted in overglaze iron-red, brown and gilding with two chinoiserie scenes, one depicting 'Boy in the Window'. The cover with stylised floral sprays, border patterns around the neck and edge of the cover. Footrim to base.

103 CREAM PAIL AND LADLE

Porcelain

Richard Chaffers, Liverpool c.1757–60

h. pail 3 ⅜ in (86) l. ladle 5in (127mm)

Elaborately moulded pail and ladle. The pail with scrolled and foliate cartouche panels on each side topped by a shell motif, the moulded scroll handle with shell terminal and the whole raised on four shell-moulded feet. The ladle with ribbed exterior and the handle with raised decoration. Overglaze enamel painted in red, green and grey with stylised floral sprays and other motifs.

104 CREAM JUG

Porcelain

Richard Chaffers, Liverpool c.1758–60

h. 3 ¾ in (95mm)

Faceted jug of pear-shape with rococo-scroll handle. Both sides decorated in polychrome enamels with the 'Stag Hunt' pattern. Flat base.

105 SAUCEBOAT

Porcelain
Richard Chaffers, Liverpool c.1760

l. 7¼in (184mm)
Moulded sauceboat of silver-shape with rococo scrollwork and foliate moulding above foot. Scroll handle with thumb-rest. The exterior decorated with a chinoiserie scene on each side, painted in underglaze blue, overglaze red enamel and gilding. The interior with a 'famille verte' stylised flower and scroll panel in the centre in polychrome enamels and with four stylised flower and insect motifs on the inside rim in iron-red and gilding. Flat base.

106 BOWL

Porcelain
Richard Chaffers, Liverpool c.1758-60

d. 4¾in (120mm)
Fluted bowl on raised foot, having an unglazed base with wide footrim. The exterior incised with scrollwork and painted in bright translucent enamel colours with three chinoiserie scenes with figures. Chain-link border pattern in iron-red and gilding around the inside rim.

107 JUG

Porcelain
Richard Chaffers, Liverpool c.1758-60

h. 6⅝in (168mm)
Of pear-shape on a rounded foot with plain strap handle. Overglaze painted in poly-chrome enamels with various exotic birds including a peacock. Broad shallow footrim to base.

108 FIGURE: NUN

Porcelain

Richard Chaffers, Liverpool c.1758–60

h. 5in (127mm)

Slip-cast moulded figure of a seated nun reading a book, in the white. Flat base with a small vent hole and a number '3' incised to one side.

109 COFFEE CAN

Porcelain

Richard Chaffers, Liverpool c.1760

h. 2³⁄₈in (60mm)

Of straight-sided form, very slightly flaring out at the foot and with a plain strap handle. Overglaze painted in poly-chrome enamels with a floral spray of roses and other flowers. Footrim to base.

110 JUG

Porcelain

Philip Christian,
Liverpool c.1765–70

h. 4in (102mm)

Pear-shaped on a low foot with a pointed sparrow-beak lip and moulded double-scroll handle. The exterior with moulded decoration of cartouche panels against a pleated or fluted ground, further decorated with flowers and foliage. The cartouche panels decorated in underglaze blue with two chinoiserie scenes and with a stylised floral motif below the lip. Lattice border pattern around the inside and outside rim. Footrim to base.

111 PLATE

Porcelain

Philip Christian, Liverpool c.1770

d. 9¼in (235mm)

Painted in underglaze blue with a peony, bamboo and stylised rock pattern. The central design surrounded by a band of diaper pattern and with three floral sprays around the rim. The reverse plain with recessed base.

112 SWEETMEAT DISH

Porcelain

Philip Christian, Liverpool c.1770

l. 4in (102mm)

A pair of sweetmeat dishes, each moulded in the form of a shell and decorated with stylised floral sprays, painted in underglaze blue.

113 CREAM EWER

Porcelain

Philip Christian, Liverpool c.1775

h. 2¾in (70mm)

Moulded in the form of a shell on a flared foot, and with a 'lamprey' handle. The shell moulding painted in underglaze blue. Footrim to base.

114 MUG

Porcelain
Philip Christian, Liverpool c.1765-68

h. 4³⁄₄ in (121mm)

Of slightly tapering cylindrical shape, and strap handle with out-turned lower terminal. Painted in underglaze blue with a chinoiserie scene depicting a fisherman with rod beside Chinese fence and willow tree. Lattice border pattern around outside rim. Flat base with chamfered edge.

115 GUGLET

Porcelain
Philip Christian, Liverpool c.1770-75

h. 11¹⁄₄in (286mm)

Of ovoid shape tapering to narrow neck with slightly flared-out rim. The exterior painted in underglaze blue with a chinoiserie landscape with pagodas, twisted rocks, willow tree and Chinese fence. Diaper border pattern around the rim exterior. Footrim to base.

116 TEAPOT AND COVER, SAUCER FRAGMENT

Porcelain
Philip Christian, Liverpool c.1768-72

h. 6in (152mm)

Teapot of globular shape with ribbed loop handle and plain spout. The domed cover with pointed ball knop. Decorated on both sides with peony, bamboo and stylised rock-form beside fence, painted in underglaze blue. Footrim to base. The biscuit saucer fragment, painted with the same pattern, was recovered from Richmond Row, Liverpool in July 1968.

117 ASPARAGUS SERVER

Porcelain
Philip Christian, Liverpool c.1765–68

l. 3-3/8 in (86mm)
The interior painted in underglaze blue
with a floral design. The pierced sides
with feather-edged moulding, high-lighted
in blue.

118 TEA BOWL AND SAUCER, FRAGMENTS

Porcelain
Philip Christian, Liverpool 1766

d. saucer 5-3/8 in (137mm)
d. teabowl 3in (76mm)
Underglaze blue painted with a 'tufted'
bird on a flowering branch and with a
lattice border pattern around the inside
rim. Inscribed 'WS / 1766' on both tea
bowl and saucer. The two biscuit fragments,
also from a tea bowl and saucer, decorated
with a similar pattern in underglaze blue.
Both were recovered from Richmond
Row, Liverpool in July 1968.

119 SAUCEBOAT

Porcelain
Philip Christian, Liverpool c.1772–78

l. 4-7/8 in (124mm)
A silver-shaped sauceboat moulded with
three arched panels on each side and
with gadrooning around the outside rim.
Underglaze blue printed on both sides
with peony and fence beside rock and
willow tree. Floral sprigs on the lip and
in the centre of the interior.

120 MUG
Porcelain
Philip Christian, Liverpool c.1770-78

h. 7¹/₂in (190mm)
Large cylindrical mug having a moulded
double-scroll handle with comma terminal.
Underglaze blue printed with peony,
bamboo and Chinese fence pattern on
one side and a pagoda and rocky island
on the other. Broad band of cell pattern
around the rim exterior. Flat base with
chamfered edge.

121 MUG
Porcelain
Philip Christian, Liverpool 1768
Printed by John Sadler, Liverpool

h. 3⁷/₈in (98mm)
Mug of cylindrical form having a strap
handle with out-turned lower terminal.
Overglaze transfer-printed in black with
'Harvest Home' or 'The Haymakers' on
one side, and with the 'Flute Player, Lady
and Children' on the other. Flat base with
chamfered edge. Dated 'Feb 9 / 1768' in
cursive script in black enamel.

122 SPOON TRAY
Porcelain
Philip Christian, Liverpool c.1770-78

l. 6in (152mm)
Of fluted form, overglaze painted in
polychrome enamels with chinoiserie
figures, furniture and vases. Line, scallop
and dot border pattern in iron-red
around the inside rim. Flat base.

120

121

122

123 COFFEE POT AND COVER

Porcelain

Philip Christian, Liverpool c.1770-78

h. 10in (254mm)

Of pear-shape on rounded foot with moulded spout and double-scroll handle with comma terminal. The high domed cover with pointed conical knop. Overglaze painted in polychrome enamels with a chinoiserie design on both sides depicting three figures, furniture and vases. Line, scallop and dot border in iron-red below rim of coffee pot and around edge of cover. Footrim to base.

124 COFFEE CUP

Porcelain

Philip Christian, Liverpool c.1768-72

h. 2 1/2in (63mm)

Coffee cup of cylindrical shape curving to low foot and with grooved loop handle. Overglaze painted in polychrome enamels and gilding with a scene depicting two chinoiserie figures. The central design flanked by a scrolled cartouche and three oval panels reserved against a gilded patterned ground. Iron-red stylised leaf motif in the centre of the interior. Footrim to base.

125 TEA BOWL AND SAUCER
Porcelain
Philip Christian, Liverpool c.1765-70

d. saucer 5in (127mm)
d. tea bowl 3 1/16 in (77mm)
Overglaze painted in polychrome
enamels with a 'tufted' bird on flowering
branch sprouting from a blue hollow
rock. Line and scallop border in iron-red
around inside rim. Floral motif in centre
of tea bowl interior beside two smaller
leaf motifs. Footrim to base.

126 VASE AND COVER
Porcelain
Philip Christian, Liverpool c.1768-72

h. 8 1/2 in (216mm)
Vase of baluster form with domed cover
and pointed conical knop. Overglaze
painted in polychrome enamels with
floral sprays and sprigs within shaped
panels. The panels outlined in gilt and
reserved against a brushed ground in
underglaze blue. Footrim to base.

127 TEAPOT AND COVER
Porcelain
Philip Christian, Liverpool c.1768-72

h. 6in (152mm)
Of faceted, globular shape with faceted
spout and ribbed loop handle. The
slightly domed, faceted cover with
pointed button knop. Overglaze painted
in polychrome enamels with two

chinoiserie scenes: one depicting the 'Beckoning Chinaman', the other with two figures, one with fan, beside a twisted rock and tree. The cover decorated with stylised floral motifs. Footrim to base.

128 SAUCEBOAT
Porcelain
Philip Christian, Liverpool c.1772–78

l. 5⅝ in (143mm)
Silver-shaped sauceboat, relief-moulded with three arched panels on each side. Overglaze enamel painted in poly-chrome with an exotic bird and with stylised floral motifs on the lip and the centre of the interior. The edge of the rim and handle high-lighted in puce. Oval footrim to base.

129 JUG
Porcelain
Probably Seth Pennington, Liverpool 1785

h. 6¹¹⁄₁₆ in (170mm)
Of bulbous form on a flared foot and with a moulded scroll handle. Decorated in underglaze blue with two mounted warriors with raised swords, on one side, and on the other with three sailing ships. The scallop border around the outside rim having run during the firing. The handle with a husk pattern. The base inscribed in blue 'M / WE / 1785'.

130 COFFEE CUP, TEA BOWL FRAGMENT

Porcelain

Seth Pennington, Liverpool c.1785-90

h. 2³⁄₄in (70mm)

Coffee cup of tapering shape, relief-moulded with a band of scrolling flowers above spiral ribbing. Grooved loop handle. Decorated in underglaze blue with a cell and pendant border pattern around the outside rim. The tea bowl fragment, having the same moulded decoration, was recovered during the re-building of Liverpool Museum in 1961-2.

131 JUG

Porcelain

Seth Pennington, Liverpool c.1780-85

h. 9³⁄₄ in (248mm)

Of bulbous form on a flared foot, having a foliate scroll handle and moulded mask lip. Painted in underglaze blue with an elaborate border around the rim exterior and a floral pattern around the foot. The body further decorated with foliate scrollwork and inscribed '*RICHARD BRIDGE / ELTON*'. Shallow footrim to base.

132 SAUCEBOAT, FRAGMENT

Porcelain

Seth Pennington, Liverpool c.1785

h. 4¹⁄₂in (114mm)

Moulded sauceboat with scalloped rim on flared foot, and with a biting snake handle. The exterior moulded in relief with a grape and vine design incorporating

130

131

a mask and 'Liver bird' motif. Foliate moulding around the foot. Further decorated in underglaze blue with flowers and scrolls around the interior and below the lip. Footrim to base. The biscuit fragment, also from a sauceboat, shows the 'Liver bird' and grape and vine moulding. The fragment was recovered from Richmond Row, Liverpool in July 1968.

133 MUG, FRAGMENTS
Porcelain
Seth Pennington, Liverpool c.1778–85

h. 3¾in (95mm)
Small mug of slightly waisted form on a flared foot, and with a flattened loop handle. Underglaze transfer-printed in blue with the 'Three Ladies' pattern on one side, and a peony and rock design on the other. Narrow footrim to base. The biscuit fragments, from a saucer and tea bowl, also underglaze blue printed with the 'Three Ladies' pattern. They were recovered from Richmond Row, Liverpool in July 1968.

134 SAUCEBOAT
Porcelain
Seth Pennington, Liverpool c.1778–85

l. 6¾in (171mm)
A moulded sauceboat on a flared foot, moulded in relief with two cartouche panels, one on each side, against a ribbed ground. Underglaze blue printed on both sides with a peony and fence beside rock and willow tree, and with floral sprigs on the lip and in the centre of the interior.

135 CREAM JUG

Porcelain
Seth Pennington, Liverpool c.1780-90

h. 3⅜in (86mm)

Of 'Chelsea Ewer' shape with foliate and spiral moulding, and with a moulded scroll handle. Overglaze painted in polychrome enamels with an exotic bird on a branch. Iron-red line and cell border around the inside rim and with iron-red details around the foot. Slightly recessed base.

136 TEAPOT AND COVER, FRAGMENT

Porcelain
Seth Pennington, Liverpool c.1778-85

h. 6⅜in (162mm)

Of ovoid shape with palm-tree and leaf moulding around the exterior, and having a moulded spout and ribbed handle. The domed cover with pointed ovoid knop. Overglaze painted in polychrome enamels with floral sprays within the panels and on the cover. The leaves around the foot picked out in green, yellow and pink and with an iron-red border pattern of stylised flower-heads and scrolls around the rim and edge of the cover. The biscuit fragment, from the base of a similarly moulded teapot, was recovered during the re-building of Liverpool Museum in 1961-2.

137 CREAM JUG

Porcelain

Seth Pennington, Liverpool c.1785-95

h. 3¾in (95mm)

Of pear-shape on narrow foot, with moulded double-scroll handle and sparrow-beak lip. Overglaze enamel painted in iron-red, green, black, puce and yellow depicting a chinoiserie scene with two figures. Iron-red line and scallop border around inside rim. Footrim to base.

138 INKWELL AND STOPPER

Porcelain

Pennington, Liverpool c.1780-85

d. 3⅛in (80mm)

A circular inkwell with three holes for holding the pens and a hollow stopper to contain the ink. Painted in underglaze blue with floral sprays and border patterns. Flat unglazed base.

139 JUG

Porcelain

John Pennington, Liverpool 1772

h. 7¾in (197mm)

Of swollen pear shape on a flared foot and with a moulded mask lip. The moulded handle with thumb-rest and scroll terminal. The exterior underglaze painted in blue with branches of stylised flowers and foliage, a 'tufted' bird and winged insect. Inscribed '*I.H / 1772*' below the lip. Broad footrim to base.

140 JUG

Porcelain

John Pennington, Liverpool 1773

h. 9⁷/₁₆ in (240mm)

Of swelling, baluster form with an elaborate scroll handle. The relief-moulded lip in the form of a mask surrounded by scrolls and feather-like motifs. The body moulded with three bands of vertical fluting and with a band of feather-like scrolls around the rim and foot. Further decorated in relief with three cartouche panels of scrolls and flowering branches. Underglaze blue painted with stylised flowers within two of the panels and around the rim and lip and with a stylised border pattern above the foot. The central cartouche inscribed 'R / J,C, / 1773' within a stylised floral wreath. The base flat.

140

141

141 SHIP BOWL

Porcelain

Pennington, Liverpool 1779

d. 8¹/₂ in (215mm)

Underglaze blue painted, the interior with a rigged ship, inscribed '1779 / SUCCESS TO THE ISSABELLA' and with a border pattern around the inside rim. The exterior with a landscape scene with sailors beside a chest inscribed 'SPANISH GOLD'.

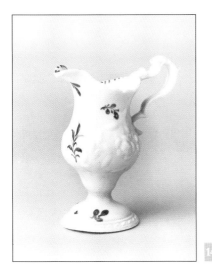

142 CREAM JUG

Porcelain

Pennington, Liverpool c.1785-95

h. 4¹/₂ in (114mm)
Silver-shaped jug on a pedestal foot, moulded with stylised flowers and leaves and having an elaborate biting-snake handle. Underglaze blue painted with stylised leaf sprays on the exterior and inside lip, and a blue-dash border around the rim interior.

143 MINIATURE COFFEE POT AND COVER, JUG

Porcelain

Pennington, Liverpool c.1780-85

h. coffee pot 4¹/₂ in (114mm)
Both of swollen pear-shape; the coffee pot on a flared foot and with a plain spout and grooved loop handle. The slightly domed cover with flange and conical knop. Underglaze blue painted with a chinoiserie scene of a house, rock and willow tree and with a scallop border pattern around the rim and edge of cover. Footrim to base.

144 COFFEE CUP

Porcelain

John Pennington, Liverpool c.1780-85

h. 2¹/₂ in (63mm)
Of cylindrical shape curving in to the foot and with a roll handle. Underglaze blue printed with a chinoiserie scene of two figures beside a willow tree, hollow rock and Chinese fence. Parts of the design painted in with a blue wash. Fine blue band painted around the inside rim. Footrim to base.

145 JUG

Porcelain
John Pennington, Liverpool 1779

h. 6⅞ in (176mm)
Of bulbous form on a flared foot and
with an everted rim with pointed lip.
The double-grooved strap handle with
out-turned lower terminal. Underglaze
decorated in blue which has run during
the firing. The main design of a scrolled
cartouche with birds, inscribed in the
centre *'FREDERICK / HEINZEL-*
MAN / LIVERPOOL / 1779' and with
two small vignettes on each side. The
one on the left showing various maritime
emblems including a crate, barrel, mast
and anchor, the one on the right depicting
a castle turret, two swans and a river. The
cartouche flanked on both sides by a lion
rampant, underglaze transfer-printed.
Cell border pattern around rim exterior,
the lip decorated with a rose spray with a
bird on each side. Broad unglazed
footrim.

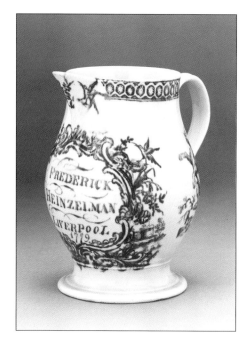

145

146 BOTTLE

Porcelain
Pennington, Liverpool c.1780

h. 5in (127mm)
Small bottle of ovoid shape tapering to a
narrow neck with cupped rim and
standing on a flared foot. Underglaze
blue printed with two floral sprays, one
including a fruit.

146

147 BUTTER BOAT
Porcelain
Pennington, Liverpool c.1780-85

l. 3⅜ in (86mm)
A small moulded boat of leaf-shape with squared handle. The interior underglaze blue printed with a border pattern and with a motif in the centre. The exterior undecorated.

148 PICKLE DISH
Porcelain
John Pennington, Liverpool c.1785-90

l. 5⅜ in (137mm)
A moulded leaf-shaped dish on three small feet. The interior underglaze blue printed with a chinoiserie landscape with pagodas and two figures on a bridge. The edge of the rim painted with a wash of underglaze blue.

149 SAUCEBOAT
Porcelain
Pennington, Liverpool c.1780

l. 5⅜ in (137mm)
Plain moulded form having a handle with thumb-rest and out-turned lower terminal. Overglaze transfer-printed in grey-black with a three-masted ship on one side, a scene with two ships on the other and with a floral spray below the lip. The handle, inside lip and centre of interior decorated in black enamel with stylised motifs. Flat, partially glazed base.

150 TEA BOWL AND SAUCER
Porcelain
Probably John Pennington, Liverpool
c.1780–85

d. saucer 4¾in (121mm)
Overglaze painted in polychrome enamels
with a chinoiserie scene depicting four
figures, including a seated man next to a
fishing rod. Scallop and line border
pattern in iron-red around inside rim.
Footrim to base.

151 JUG
Porcelain
Pennington, Liverpool c.1785-95

h. 4in (102mm)
Of inverted helmet shape on a pedestal
foot and with a biting-snake handle.
Overglaze enamel painted in polychrome depicting two Chinese figures
beside a tree and with a 'famille rose'
type border around the inside rim.

152 VASE AND COVER
Porcelain
Pennington, Liverpool c.1780-90

h. 10³⁄₈in (264mm)
Baluster-shaped vase having a domed
cover with 'lion' knop. Underglaze
painted in blue with reserved panels and
a scale pattern border. The panels
decorated in overglaze enamels with
polychrome floral sprays and with traces
of gilding. Footrim to base.

153

154

153 COFFEE CAN
Porcelain
Possibly John Pennington, Liverpool
c.1775–85

h. 2⅜ in (60mm)
Of cylindrical form with small roll handle and flat unglazed base. Overglaze painted in polychrome enamels with flowering branches sprouting from stylised rock-work.

154 COFFEE POT AND COVER, HANDLE FRAGMENT
Porcelain
John Pennington, Liverpool c.1775–85

h. 10in (254mm)
Of swollen pear-shape on a flared foot with a plain spout. The moulded double-scroll handle with foliate thumb-rest and comma terminal. The domed cover having a ball knop with pointed finial. Overglaze painted in polychrome enamels with floral sprays and sprigs. The handle high-lighted in iron-red and the spout with feather motifs. Underglaze blue and gilded scallop border around the neck and edge of cover. Broad footrim to base. The matching biscuit handle fragment was recovered from Upper Islington during demolition and roadworks in 1968.

155 TEAPOT AND COVER

Porcelain
Pennington, Liverpool c.1780-90

h. 6$\frac{1}{2}$in (165mm)

Of globular shape with ribbed loop handle and plain spout. The slightly domed cover with pointed knop. Overglaze enamel painted in polychrome with floral sprays and smaller sprigs and with a 'famille rose' border pattern around the neck and edge of the cover. Stylised floral motif in iron-red down the handle. Inscribed *'Alice Adkinson'*, painted in black enamel. Shallow footrim to base.

156 CREAM JUG

Porcelain
Liverpool c.1785-90

h. 3in (76mm)

Cream jug of high 'Chelsea Ewer' form with foliate moulding above the foot and with a moulded handle. Overglaze painted in polychrome enamels with two Chinese figures standing on each side of a tree and with a scallop and line border below the rim interior in iron-red. *'HP'* painted in underglaze blue on base.

157 TEA BOWL AND SAUCER

Porcelain
Liverpool c.1785-95

d. saucer 5$\frac{1}{4}$in (133mm)

Painted in polychrome enamels with a number of sprigs of roses and other flowers. Fine brown banding around the rim on both tea bowl and saucer. Footrim to base. *'HP'* painted in underglaze blue on base.

155

156

157

158 SUGAR BOX AND COVER, COFFEE CAN, FRAGMENT

Porcelain

Thomas Wolfe & Co., Liverpool c.1796–1800

h. sugar box 5³⁄₄in (146mm)
h. coffee can 2¹⁄₂in (63mm)
Sugar box of oval section with moulded ring handles. Both sugar box and coffee can underglaze blue printed with the 'Dagger Border' pattern and further decorated with gilding. The unglazed fragment, probably from an oval teapot stand, is underglaze blue printed with the same pattern. It was recovered from Upper Islington, Liverpool during demolition and roadworks in 1968.

159 TEAPOT AND COVER, COFFEE CUP, FRAGMENTS

Porcelain

Thomas Wolfe & Co., Liverpool c.1796–1800

h. teapot 6in (152mm)
h. coffee cup 2¹⁄₂in (63mm)
Teapot of oval section with straight spout. The teapot and coffee cup under-glaze blue printed with the 'Gardener' pattern. The coffee cup further decorated with gilding around the rim, foot and down the handle. The biscuit saucer fragments underglaze blue printed with the same pattern. The cover fragment matches in shape but is decorated with the 'Dagger Border' pattern. All fragments were recovered from Upper Islington, Liverpool during demolition and road-works in 1968.

160 SAUCER, CREAMER, FRAGMENT

Porcelain

Thomas Wolfe & Co., Liverpool c.1796-1800

d. saucer 5 1/8 in (130mm)
h. creamer 4 1/2 in (114mm)
Underglaze blue printed with the
'Empty Wooden Bridge' pattern, the
creamer further decorated with gilding
around the rim and down the handle.
The unglazed fragment, probably from a
tea bowl, showing part of the same
pattern. The fragment was recovered
from Upper Islington, Liverpool during
demolition and roadworks in 1968.

160

161 PLATE, FRAGMENTS

Porcelain

Thomas Wolfe & Co., Liverpool c.1796-1800

d. 9 1/2 in (241mm)
Underglaze blue printed with the
'Temple Landscape' pattern, depicting a
chinoiserie scene within a band of
diaper pattern alternating with four
floral panels. The rim decorated with
a complex border pattern. The two
biscuit plate fragments, of smaller
scale, underglaze printed with the
same pattern. Both were recovered
from Upper Islington, Liverpool
during demolition and roadworks
in 1968.

161

162 CREAMER, SLOP BOWL, FRAGMENTS

Porcelain
Thomas Wolfe & Co., Liverpool c.1796–1800

h. creamer 4 3/8 in (112mm)
Underglaze blue printed with the 'Love Birds and Wooden Bridge' pattern, depicting a chinoiserie scene around the exterior and a complex border pattern at the rim. The biscuit saucer fragment showing a portion of the same printed design; the glazed fragment from the rim of a cup decorated with the same border pattern. Both fragments were recovered from Upper Islington, Liverpool during demolition and road-works in 1968.

163 TEAPOT AND COVER, COFFEE CUP, FRAGMENTS

Porcelain
Thomas Wolfe & Co., Liverpool c.1796–1800

h. teapot 6 1/2 in (165mm)
The teapot of oval section with fluted sides, and having a curved spout. The moulded handle with thumb-rest. The coffee cup of fluted cylindrical form curving in to low foot. Both underglaze blue printed with the 'Shuttered Window' pattern and with gilt banding. The teapot further decorated in gilding with a pendant and swag border below the shoulder. The biscuit porcelain fragments, from a saucer and a cover, underglaze blue printed with the same design. They were both recovered from Upper Islington, Liverpool during demolition and roadworks in 1968.

164 CREAMER, COFFEE CUP, FRAGMENTS

Porcelain

Thomas Wolfe & Co., Liverpool c.1796–1800

h. creamer 4¼ in (108mm)

h. cup 2½ in (63mm)

A creamer and cup moulded with spiral fluting. Painted in polychrome enamels with a basket of flowers and floral sprigs and with simple borders of dots and fine banding. The undecorated biscuit fragment from a similarly moulded cup. The enamel painted fragment, probably from a tea bowl, decorated with the same pattern. Both fragments were recovered from Upper Islington, Liverpool during demolition and roadworks in 1968.

164

165 COFFEE CUP

Creamware
Wedgwood, Staffordshire c.1775
Printed in Liverpool

h. 2¾in (70mm)
Shell-edge moulding below rim exterior.
The double-loop intertwined handles
with foliate upper-terminals and curled
ends. Transfer-printed in puce with 'exotic'
birds, also referred to as 'Liverpool birds'.
Footrim to base. Faintly impressed
'*WEDGWOOD*' on base.

166 JUG

Creamware
Possibly Herculaneum, Liverpool 1798
Printed in Liverpool

h. 9½in (241mm)
Of tall baluster form with plain loop
handle and pointed lip. Overglaze transfer-
printed in black with a variety of subjects;
below the lip the 'Farmers Arms'
surmounted by an arch of scrolls and
flowering stems containing the inscription
'*LCD /1798*' painted in black enamel.
To the right, a print depicting the
'Blacksmiths' Arms' above a floral spray of
a tulip and other flowers. The other side
with a harvest scene of merry-making,
above another flower spray of honeysuckle
and convulvulus. Below the handle, a
motto within an oval frame. Further
transfer-prints of swags of grapes and
vine leaves and various flowers around
the rim exterior. The edge of the rim
banded in green and black enamel.
Footrim to base.

167 BEAKER

Glass
Printed in Liverpool c.1790-1800

h. 3⅝in (93mm)
Semi-opaque white glass beaker of
tapering straight-sided form. Transfer-
printed in black with a version of 'The
Farmyard' and with a floral spray.

168 MUG

Creamware
Wedgwood, Staffordshire c.1765-70
Printed by John Sadler, Liverpool

h. 4⅞in (124mm)
Of cylindrical shape with loop handle.
Overglaze black transfer-printed with
the arms of the Society of Bucks, signed
'Sadler Liverpool', and flanked by prints of
two angels representing 'Justice' on the
right, and 'Fame' on the left. Narrow
footrim to base.

169 TILE

Tin-glazed earthenware
Liverpool c.1757-61
Printed by John Sadler, Liverpool

l. 5in (127mm)
Overglaze transfer-printed in red from a
copper-plate with the arms of the
Society of Bucks, signed on the bottom
right 'J. Sadler'.

167

168

169

170 MUG

Porcelain
Richard Chaffers, Liverpool 1763
Printed by John Sadler, Liverpool

h. 6¼ in (159mm)
Of straight-sided form, flaring out slightly at foot and having a plain strap handle with out-turned lower terminal. Transfer-printed in black with the arms of the Society of Bucks. The flat unglazed base incised *'James Hayes 1763'* in cursive script.

James Hayes, potter, appears in the Parish register of St. Peter's Liverpool on the 24 January 1762 when his twin daughters, Martha and Catherine were baptised.

171 MUG

Porcelain
Longton Hall, Staffordshire c.1760-65
Printed by John Sadler, Liverpool

h. 3¾ in (95mm)
Of barrel-shape on a slightly flared foot, having a moulded scroll handle with thumb-rest. Overglaze transfer-printed in black with the arms of the Society of Bucks, signed *'Sadler Liverpool'*, flanked by two angels representing 'Justice' on the right and 'Fame' on the left. Footrim to base.

172 BADGE

Enamel on copper alloy
Printed in Liverpool c.1760

l. 3¼in (83mm)
Of oval shape within a metal frame, probably the regalia of a 'Forester'. Transfer-printed in black; one side showing a hunter shooting a deer within a cartouche. The cartouche flanked by the figures of 'Time' and 'Flora' surmounted by a beehive, the words *'Learn by Example', 'Trust in God'* and *'Adhere to Virtue'* within scrolled ribbons. On the other side, two peasants carrying a fox within an ornate rococo cartouche, also enclosing a mace and sword and the words *'Avoid Ridicule'*.

173 COFFEE POT AND COVER

Creamware
Probably Wedgwood, Staffordshire c.1770
Printed in Liverpool

h. 9in (228mm)
Of pear-shape having a reeded strap handle with foliate terminal and ribbed spout with leaf moulding around the base. The slightly domed cover with flange and pierced-ball knop. Transfer-printed in black, on one side with a version of 'The Shepherd' depicting a seated figure with dog and sheep in a rural setting. The other side printed with a scrolled cartouche, black enamel painted in the centre with the inscription *'I.HARRIS, / WESTWOOD'*. The cover decorated with various prints of floral sprigs and a butterfly. Flat base, partially glazed.

172

173

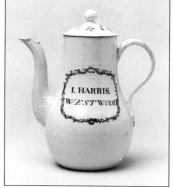

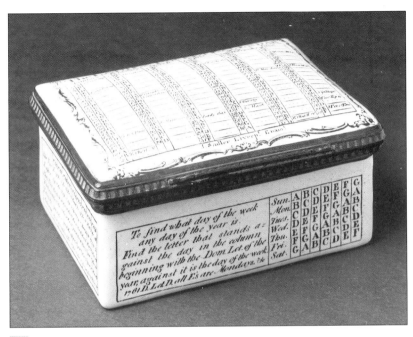

174 BOX

Enamel on copper alloy
Printed by John Sadler, Liverpool c.1760

l. 3 1/8 in (79mm)

Rectangular box with hinged lid. Transfer-printed in black with *'The LADIES POCKET KALENDAR'*, signed *'J.Sadler Liverpl. Enaml'*. The lid printed with the months January to June, and the base, July to September. The inscription on the front panel gives directions how *'To find what day of the week /any day of the year is'*. On the back panel, there is a guide to the lunar and solar cycles, and the side panels give the dates of the main religious days for the years 1760–77.

175 PLAQUE

Enamel on copper alloy
Printed in Liverpool c.1760

l. 3 1/8 in (79mm)

An oval plaque within a beaded gilt metal frame. Transfer-printed in black with *'Caffee'* after J.E. Nilson, showing a seated gentleman at ease with a long stemmed pipe, breakfasting with a lady. The whole scene surrounded by flowered rococo scrolls.

(see E.C.C. *'Transactions'* Vol.9 Pt.1 p.53–54)

176 TEAPOT

Creamware
Wedgwood, Staffordshire c.1770-80
Printed by Guy Green, Liverpool

h. 3⁷⁄₈in (98mm)
Of spherical form with overlapping leaf
or scale handle, and moulded cabbage
spout. Cover lacking. Overglaze transfer-
printed in black; one side with a portrait
of John Wesley flanked by a scroll inscribed
*'JOHN WESLEY. M.A. FELLOW OF
/ LINCOLN COLLEGE, OXFORD'.*
The print signed *'Green, Liverpool'*. The
reverse side printed with a religious
inscription, *'Let your / Conversation be /
as becometh / the Gospel of / Christ'* within
a cartouche of scrolls and flowering
stems and with two small religious scenes
on each side. One depicting St Peter
praying and the other, the Good Samaritan.
Flat base.

176

177 TILE

Tin-glazed earthenware
Liverpool c.1775
Printed by Guy Green, Liverpool

l. 5in (127mm)
Overglaze transfer-printed in black with
three Chinese figures beside a letter from
a 'chinoiserie alphabet', signed *'Green'* in
the bottom right, the '88' border. This is
the only tile design recorded with the
signature of Green. The scene is taken
from Pillement's *'Petit Parasols Chinois'*
which was published in 1774.
(see E.C.C. *'Transactions'* Vol.9 Pt.1 p.61)

177

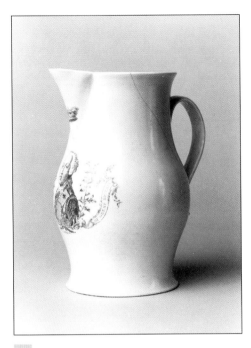

178 JUG

Porcelain
Richard Chaffers, Liverpool c.1760-65
Printed by John Sadler, Liverpool

h. 7 1/8 in (181mm)
Of baluster shape having a strap handle
with out-turned lower terminal. Flat
unglazed base. Overglaze transfer-printed
in grey-black with a portrait flanked by
scrolled ribbons, inscribed *'GEORGE III
KING / OF GREAT BRITAIN'*, signed
'T. Billinge Sc', and with a small crown
printed on the lip exterior.

179 MUG

Porcelain
Worcester c.1760-65
Printed by John Sadler, Liverpool

h. 4 3/4 in (121mm)
Of straight-sided form with broad
footrim to base and having a ribbed loop
handle. Overglaze transfer-printed in
black with a portrait inscribed
*'Fred,ye:III:d / KING OF PRUSSIA /
Elector of Brandenbourg'*, signed *'Gilbody
Maker / Evans Sc'*. The portrait flanked
by prints of angels depicting 'Fame' on
the right and 'Justice' on the left. The
edge of the rim finely banded in iron-red.

This mug has caused past controversy.
Although signed *'Gilbody Maker'*, analysis
has confirmed it to be of Worcester
porcelain. The confusing situation would
appear to be the result of John Sadler
using a Gilbody copper-plate, without
removing the signature, to decorate a
Worcester blank.

180 PLATE

Creamware
Probably Wedgwood, Staffordshire c.1780-90
Printed in Liverpool

d. 10in (254mm)
Of 'Royal' shape, transfer-printed in
black with a rustic scene in the centre
depicting a man seated on a wooden
bridge over a stream, talking to a shepherdess who is driving two sheep across
the bridge. The print signed *'Joseph
Johnson Liverpool'*. The rim printed with
six floral sprays. Very narrow footrim to
reverse.

181 MUG

Creamware
Printed in Liverpool c.1789

h. 4in (102mm)
Cylindrical shape with plain loop handle.
Overglaze transfer-printed in black with
*'The East View of Liverpool Lighthouse and
Signals on Bidston Hill 1789'*, signed
'Printed by Josh.Johnson Liverpool'.

182 JUG

Creamware
Probably printed in Liverpool c.1810

h. 8⅞in (225mm)
Of swollen baluster form with plain loop
handle. Overglaze transfer-printed in
black with the *'SIGNALS AT /
PORTLAND / OBSERVATORY'*, on
one side; the other side transfer-printed
with two three-masted ships flying the
American flag, one ship inscribed
'WASHINGTON'. Both prints decorated

Enamel bands around the outside rim and above the foot.

In 1807 an observatory was erected on the highest hill in Portland, Maine, U.S.A., for the purpose of warning the town of approaching ships. The structure was a lighthouse-like building, capped by a dome having two signal staffs, one on the east side and one on the west.

183 BEAKER

Glass
Printed in Liverpool c.1788

h. 3¾ in (96mm)

Semi-opaque white glass beaker of tapering straight-sided form. Black transfer-printed decoration inscribed *'An East View of Liverpool Light House & Signals on Bidston Hill 1788'*.

The print depicting the signalling system adopted to give early warning of approaching vessels. This example lists 44 signal flag combinations.

184 MUG

Porcelain
Richard Chaffers, Liverpool c.1760
Printed by John Sadler, Liverpool

h. 4⅞ in (124mm)

Of straight-sided shape, slightly flared at foot and with a plain strap handle with out-turned lower terminal. Overglaze transfer-printed in black with *'The Tythe Pig'* with verse below. The design is from an engraving of 1751 by Müller after Boitard. (see E.C.C. *'Transactions'* Vol.9 Pt.1 p.56). Flat, partially glazed base.

185 MUG

Creamware
Probably Wedgwood, Staffordshire c.1763
Printed by John Sadler, Liverpool

h. 6¾in (171mm)
Of cylindrical form having a reeded
handle with foliate lower terminal.
Overglaze transfer-printed in red with
'The Tythe Pig', with verse below, after a
print of that name published in 1751
drawn by Boitard and engraved by
Müller. Footrim to base.
See David Drakard, *'Printed English Pottery'*
p.72 for a full transcript of the verse.

186 TILE

Tin-glazed earthenware
Liverpool c.1758-61
Printed by John Sadler, Liverpool

l. 5in (127mm)
Black transfer-printed decoration of
'The Tythe Pig' within a rococo scroll
border.

187 MUG

Tin-glazed earthenware
Liverpool c.1762
Printed by John Sadler, Liverpool

h. 4⅝in (118mm)
Of very slightly waisted, cylindrical
form, having a loop handle with central
rib. Overglaze transfer-printed in black
with *'The Tythe Pig'*, signed *'Sadler
Liverpool'*, with verse below. Slightly
concave, glazed base.

188 SHIP BOWL
Creamware
Probably printed by Guy Green,
Liverpool 1782

d. 8 ¾ in (222mm)
The interior overglaze transfer-printed
in black with a three masted ship, further
decorated in enamels in black, green,
yellow and red. Painted in black with an
inscription below, *'Success to the Bridget /
John and Betty Hurst / 1782'* and with a
stylised scroll and leaf border pattern
around inside rim. The exterior with four
black transfer-prints: a portrait of
Rodney, inscribed *'SR. G. BRIDGES
RODNEY. BT. / REAR ADMIRAL OF
ENGLAND'* within a scrolled ribbon; a
scene depicting the 'sailor's farewell' within
a scrolled border, and a verse within a
scrolled panel. The final print of a motto
within an elaborate cartouche of scrolls
and flowering stems incorporating the
words *'May British Tars / ever Support the
Glory / of Old England'*.

189 PUNCH POT AND COVER
Creamware
Printed by John Sadler, Liverpool c.1770

h. 7 ⅛ in (180mm)
A two quart punch pot of globular shape
with moulded foliate spout and scroll
handle. The slightly curved cover with
pierced baluster knop. Overglaze transfer-
printed in black; one side decorated with
a rural landscape, signed *'J. Sadler, Liverpool'*
at the bottom left. The reverse printed
with a harvest scene with figures known
as 'Harvest Home' (from a print of that

name engraved by June after a design by Grimm, published by Robert Sayer of Fleet Street) or 'The Haymakers'. The cover decorated with variety of small prints including floral sprigs and insects. Flat base, with traces of glaze.

190 MUG

Creamware
Possibly Herculaneum, Liverpool c.1800
Printed in Liverpool

h. 4¾in (121mm)
Of cylindrical shape with a loop handle with ridges. Overglaze transfer-printed in black with a seated drinker or toper known as 'Toby Fillpot'; above four lines of verse. The print signed *'R. Abbey Sculpt'*. Black enamel band around rim exterior. Footrim to base.
The design is from a drawing by Robert Dighton, published as a mezzotint by Carrington Bowles and entitled *'Toby Fillpot - a thirsty old soul'* in his 1786 print catalogue. A later print of 1796 included the poem, *'The Brown Jug'*, four lines of which appear on this mug (see David Drakard *'Printed English Pottery'* p.89).

191 TILE

Tin-glazed earthenware
Liverpool c.1777–80
Printed in Liverpool

l. 5in (127mm)
Overglaze transfer-printed in black with a theatrical design entitled *'MR FOOTE in the Character of the DOCTOR / in the Devil upon Two Sticks'*, surrounded by a swag of husk pattern with two masks below, signed *'Abbey Liverpool'*.

192 MUG

Creamware
Probably Liverpool c.1775-80
Printed in Liverpool

h. 6¼in (159mm)
Of cylindrical shape with plain loop handle. Overglaze transfer-printed with a view of Liverpool entitled, in ribbon above, *'NORTH EAST VIEW / OF ST. NICHOLAS' CHURCH / LIVERPOOL'.*
The print on this mug is an unrecorded view of the Parish Church of Liverpool, showing part of the docks. In 1746 a spire was built on top of the old tower and 1774 the body of the church was rebuilt. This engraving records this new structure. In 1810 the spire collapsed into the church, killing many people.

193 TEAPOT AND COVER

Porcelain
Philip Christian, Liverpool c.1770
Printed in Liverpool

h. 6in (153mm)
Of globular shape on inwardly tapering foot, with plain curved spout and roll handle. The slightly domed cover with onion knop. Overglaze transfer-printed in red with the 'Tea Party', the body with two different sized prints. The cover printed with a much smaller version of the 'Tea Party' and with a chinoiserie subject of a seated boy with bird. Dot, scallop and line border pattern in iron-red around the neck and edge of the cover. Footrim to base.

194 PLATE

Creamware
Wedgwood, Staffordshire c.1780
Printed in Liverpool

d. 9 ⁷/₈ in (251mm)
Of royal shape, transfer-printed in black
in the centre with a rustic scene with
figures, one playing the flute, a dog, a
cow and three sheep beside stone ruins.
The rim decorated with a running border
of oak leaves and acorns.
Impressed *'WEDGWOOD'* on reverse.

195 TILE

Tin-glazed earthenware
Liverpool c.1756-7
Printed by John Sadler, Liverpool

l. 4 ¹³/₁₆ in (122mm)
Blue transfer-printed woodblock tile
depicting a gallant, wearing a hat with a
large feather, addressing a seated lady.
The design is from a series of engravings,
'Caffe, The und Tabac Zieretten' by
J.E. Nilson of Augsburg.
(see E.C.C. *'Transactions'* Vol.9 Pt.1 p53-54)

196 TILE

Tin-glazed earthenware
Liverpool c.1756-7
Printed by John Sadler, Liverpool

l. 5in (127mm)
Transfer-printed in dark manganese-brown
from a woodblock with a girl and a shepherd
with a crook. The design is from a series
of engravings entitled *'Caffe, The und
Tabac Zieretten'* by J.E. Nilson of Augsburg.
(see E.C.C. *'Transactions'* Vol.9 Pt.1 p53-54)

197 TILE
Tin-glazed earthenware
Liverpool c.1756–7
Printed by John Sadler, Liverpool

l. 4⅞in (123mm)
Blue transfer-printed woodblock tile
depicting a terrace with ruined columns.

198 TILE
Tin-glazed earthenware
Liverpool c.1756–7
Printed by John Sadler, Liverpool

l. 5in (126mm)
Transfer-printed in brown-black from a
woodblock with a 'Shepherd and
Shepherdess with Dog', within a scroll
border, further coloured in overglaze
enamels.
The design, adapted in reverse, from an
engraving by Duclos after Boucher's
picture *'Les Amours Pastorales'*.
(see E.C.C. *'Transactions'* Vol.9 Pt.1 p.55)

199 TILE
Tin-glazed earthenware
Liverpool c.1758–61
Printed by John Sadler, Liverpool

l. 5⅛in (130mm)
Transfer-printed in black from a copper-
plate, depicting a scene of a gallant offering
a bird's nest to a seated girl within a
rococo scroll border, signed *'J.Sadler
Liverpl'*.

200 TILE

Tin-glazed earthenware
Liverpool c.1756-7
Printed by John Sadler, Liverpool

l. 5in (128mm)
Blue transfer-printed woodblock tile
depicting a standing girl and a seated
man, smoking a pipe in a rococo arbour.

200

201

201 TILE

Tin-glazed earthenware
Liverpool c.1757-61
Printed by John Sadler, Liverpool

l. 5in (127mm)
Transfer-printed in brown-black from a
copper-plate with 'Madamoiselle
Camargo Dancing to pipe and drum',
signed *'J.Sadler Liverpl'*.
The design adapted from Laurent Cars'
engraving of a picture in the Wallace
Collection by Lancret.
(see E.C.C. *'Transactions'* Vol.9 Pt.1 p.55)

202

202 TILE

Tin-glazed earthenware
Liverpool c.1756-7
Printed by John Sadler, Liverpool

l. 5in (127mm)
Blue transfer-printed woodblock tile
depicting a rural scene with a building in
the background, and a man on a donkey
in the foreground. The scene within an
octagonal panel surrounded by a 'Louis
XV' border pattern.

203 TILE

Tin-glazed earthenware
Liverpool c.1761-65

l. 5in (128mm)
Transfer-printed in black from a copper-plate with the 'Tea Party', further coloured in overglaze enamels.
The design taken from the John Bowles drawing book, sheet 63, dated 2 July 1757.
(see E.C.C. *'Transactions'* Vol.9 Pt.1 p.56)

204 TILE

Tin-glazed earthenware
Liverpool c.1758-61
Printed by John Sadler, Liverpool

l. 5in (127mm)
Transfer-printed in black from a copper-plate with 'Shepherd Lovers beneath a Tree' surrounded by a scrolled border and signed *'Sadler Liverpl'*.

205 TILE

Tin-glazed earthenware
Liverpool c.1761-65
Printed by John Sadler, Liverpool

l. 5$\frac{1}{16}$in (129mm)
Transfer-printed in black from a copper-plate, with the 'Fortune Teller', further decorated in polychrome enamels. The scene depicting a girl having her palm read by a gipsy who carries a child on her back.
The subject is adapted from a design in John Bowles drawing book, dated 24 November 1756.
(see E.C.C. *'Transactions'* Vol.9 Pt.1 p.58)

206 TILE

Tin-glazed earthenware
Liverpool c.1758-61
Printed by John Sadler, Liverpool

l. 5in (127mm)
Transfer-printed in black from a copper-plate with a scene of a gentleman helping a girl over a stile, signed *'Sadler'*, within a scrolled border.

207 TILE

Tin-glazed earthenware
Liverpool c.1758-61
Printed by John Sadler, Liverpool

l. 5in (127mm)
Transfer-printed in black from a copper-plate with a ship seen from the starboard bow under full sail in a choppy sea, signed *'Sadler Liverpool'*, within a scrolled border on three sides.

208 TILE

Tin-glazed earthenware
Liverpool c.1765-75
Printed in Liverpool

l. 5in (127mm)
Transfer-printed in manganese from a copper-plate with a scene from *Æsop's Fables*, 'The Lioness and the Fox', within a scrolled *'88'* border.

209 TILE

Tin-glazed earthenware
Liverpool c.1777-80
Printed in Liverpool

l. 5in (126mm)
Transfer-printed in black from a copper-plate with *'Mrs Mattocks as Prins. Catherine'* in Shakespeare's *Henry V*.
The print from Bell's *'Shakespeare'*, is by Grignion after Roberts, dated
1 December 1775.
(see E.C.C. *'Transactions'* Vol.9 Pt.1 p.65)

210 TILE

Tin-glazed earthenware
Liverpool c.1775-80
Printed by Guy Green,
Liverpool

l. 5 1/16 in (128mm)
Transfer-printed in black from a copper-plate depicting an elaborately shaped vase draped with a garland of flowers, and having a cover with floral knop. The design further decorated in green enamel.

211 BASKET AND STAND
Earthenware
Herculaneum, Liverpool c.1800–10

l. stand 10⅝in (270mm)
Oval shaped basket and stand with pierced rims. Simply decorated with banding and fine lining in brown enamel. Both impressed 'HERCULANEUM 2 / 01' on the base.

212 PLATE
Creamware
Herculaneum, Liverpool c.1805

d. 7⅝in (194mm)
Overglaze enamel painted in tones of blue and sepia-brown with a thistle motif in the centre and with a leaf and dot border pattern around the rim. The edge banded in blue. The reverse undecorated and without a footrim.

213 TUREEN AND COVER
Creamware
Herculaneum, Liverpool c.1805–10

h. 6¼in (159mm)
Boat-shaped tureen on oval pedestal foot, having a curved cover with oval ring knop. Overglaze enamel painted in iron-red, yellow and brown with a ribboned border pattern, the edges banded in brown and the cover surrounded by a finely painted 'leaf' design.
Impressed 'HERCULANEUM' on base.

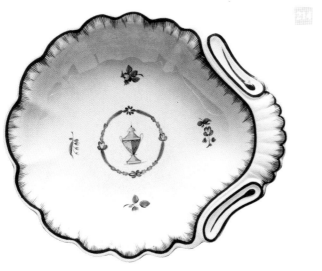

214 DESSERT DISH

Creamware

Herculaneum, Liverpool c.1805–10

l. 10in (244mm)

Shell-moulded form, overglaze enamel painted in the centre with an urn surrounded by a stylised wreath, and dotted with four flower or leaf sprigs. The rim of the dish banded in blue with a shell-edge border pattern and with a blue band around the foot.

Impressed 'HERCULANEUM' on base.

215 JUG

Creamware

Probably Herculaneum, Liverpool c.1810

h. 11¼in (286mm)

Of swelling form with plain loop handle and footrim to base. Overglaze transfer-printed in black with the Royal Arms on one side, signed in mirror image 'T. DIXON Sculpt 1803', with a floral spray below. The other side with the 'Amnesty' print commemorating the Golden Jubilee of George III, above another floral spray. The print shows a scene of released prisoners beside an equestrian statue of George III, a Liver Bird on the plinth. Above the scene are the Spirit of History and Britannia seated on clouds, supporting an inscribed scroll; another inscription appearing on a ribbon below. A further print of a floral wreath below the lip, enclosing the initials 'E & E / T' painted in black enamel with '1810' below. The edges banded in black.

216 JUG

Earthenware

Herculaneum, Liverpool c.1810-15

h. 7¹/₂ in (190mm)

Of bulbous shape with plain loop handle. Overglaze transfer-printed in puce with 'The Farmers' Arms' on one side and with a version of 'The Farmyard' on the other, signed *Joseph Johnson*. A floral sprig appears below the lip. The edges banded in black enamel and inscribed *'Robert Roberts'* in cursive script beneath the lip.

217 TOBACCO JAR AND COVER

Earthenware

Herculaneum, Liverpool c.1800

h. 9in (229mm)

Jar of cylindrical shape having a bell-shaped cover with pointed ball knop. Overglaze transfer-printed in puce with four different prints. The jar with a seascape inscribed below *'Success to the BRITISH FLEET'* and, on the other side, the inscription *'May British Tars / ever support the Glory / of Old England'* within a scrolled cartouche. The cover printed with a small scene of sailors heaving the lead and with the motto *'From Rocks & Sands / And every ill / May God preserve / the Sailor still'* within an oval frame. The whole further decorated with puce enamel banding.

218 PLATE
Creamware
Herculaneum, Liverpool c.1805
Dutch decorated

d. 9¾in (248mm)
Of 'Royal' shape, overglaze enamel painted in polychrome, the centre with a religious scene inscribed *'HET PRIESTER SCHAP'*, the rim with a foliate scroll border.
Impressed *'HERCULANEUM / 5'* on base.

219 MODEL OF A HAND
Creamware
Herculaneum, Liverpool 1812

l. 8¼in (210mm)
Moulded hand with pen, poised in the action of writing. The oval shaped base incised *'Designed for Circus Street School, Frd LEGE Sculpt. Liverpool 1812'*. Frederick Lege was an outside artist working for the Herculaneum factory and probably supplied the original mould or model to the firm. Altogether four examples are known to exist and it has been suggested that they were made as hand-writing prizes at the school.

220 TEAPOT AND COVER
Pearlware
Herculaneum, Liverpool c.1805

h. 6¼in (159mm)
Of faceted form with a scalloped rim. Relief-moulded decoration with neo-classical subjects and foliate designs, underglaze painted in 'Pratt' colours in yellow, brown, blue and green. The moulded cover with fruit or 'cushion' knop.

221 SUGAR BOX

Pearlware

Herculaneum, Liverpool c.1805

h. 4¼in (108mm)

Of faceted form, moulded in relief on each side with figures beneath a leaf-entwined arch. One figure inscribed *'APOLLO / THE GOD OF MUSIC'*, the other *'PASSION / SUBDUED BY REASON'*. The figures flanked by trailing leaves. The neck decorated with foliate moulding and with feather moulding above the foot. Painted in 'Pratt' type underglaze colours in yellow, green, orange, brown and blue with brown banding.

Impressed *'HERCULANEUM'* on base.

222 JUG

Creamware

Possibly Wedgwood, Staffordshire c.1795–1800

Decorated at Herculaneum, Liverpool

h. 9½in (242mm)

Of baluster form with plain loop handle. Overglaze painted in polychrome with a view of a mill inscribed *'SUCCESS TO MOLD / COTTON MILL'* in a ribbon above, with the Prince of Wales feather in the centre over the motto *'ICH DIEN'*. The rim exterior decorated with a running leaf-scroll border pattern in black and with green banding around the rim and on the handle.

223 PLATE

Earthenware
Herculaneum, Liverpool c.1810-15

d. 7⅞ in (200mm)
The centre overglaze painted in polychrome enamels with a rustic scene
depicting an old woman with a stick
being shown the way by a young boy.
The moulded basket-weave rim enamelled
in green, the pierced edge in purple.

224 JUG

Creamware
Herculaneum, Liverpool c.1805-10

h. 16¼ in (413mm)
Of bulbous form tapering to a ribbed
engine-turned foot. The grooved
cylindrical neck with a satyr's mask lip
and with a squared handle with foliate
terminal and mock rivets. The body
decorated with numerous transfer-prints
of various subjects including three oval
portraits of the 'Earl St Vincent', 'Lord
Duncan' and, below the lip, 'Lord Nelson',
signed *'G. Martin Sculp'*. The neck and
top of the handle enamelled in blue.

George Martin is listed in the registers of
St. Michaels-in-the-Hamlet Church,
Toxteth as a 'pottery engraver' in the
records of the births of his children by
his wife Hannah. This jug is dated after
1805 as the details of Nelson's death in
October 1805 are incorporated into the
print.

137

225 WARMING DISH

Earthenware
Herculaneum, Liverpool c.1820-5

l. 11¾in (298mm)
Underglaze blue printed in the centre with
a view of Lancaster, the rim decorated
with the 'cherub' border pattern. The
reverse with a printed scrolled cartouche,
inscribed *'LANCASTER'* in the centre.
The reverse impressed *'HERCULANEUM
21'*.

226 PIE DISH

Earthenware
Herculaneum, Liverpool c.1820-5

l. 9⅛in (232mm)
Underglaze blue printed with a view of
Conway Castle in the centre of the interior
and with a 'cherub' border pattern around
the inside and outside rims. The base
printed with a scrolled cartouche, inscribed
'CONWAY CASTLE' in the centre.
The base impressed *'HERCULANEUM'*
and *'6'* or *'9'* in large type.

227 MEAT PLATE

Earthenware
Probably Herculaneum, Liverpool c.1825-30

l. 18⅜in (467mm)
Underglaze blue printed, the centre with
a scene of Liverpool across the River
Mersey, the rim with a floral border.
The reverse blue printed with the

inscription *'[View of] the TOWN and / HARBOUR OF LIVERPOOL / [from] SEACOMBE'* within a cartouche of trees and foliage.

The view of Liverpool was copied from a print inscribed *'Engraved by T. Dixon from a painting by I. Jenkinson, published by Henry Fisher, London 1824'*.

228 PICKLE DISH

Earthenware
Herculaneum, Liverpool c.1825

l. 6$\frac{1}{4}$in (159mm)

Moulded in the form of a scallop shell, underglaze blue printed with an all-over pattern of flowers and leaves and some painted details in underglaze blue.
The reverse impressed *'HERCULANEUM'* in a semi-circle over a crown.

229 PLATE

Earthenware
Herculaneum, Liverpool c.1815-25

d. 9$\frac{1}{8}$in (232mm)

Underglaze blue printed with a rural scene in the centre, depicting three figures, cattle, sheep and a horse and with a large house in the background. The rim decorated with a floral patterned border.
The reverse printed in black with the words and music of the grace *'Non Nobis Domine'*.
The reverse impressed *'HERCULANEUM'*.

230 PLATE

Earthenware

Herculaneum, Liverpool c.1815–25

d. 9¾ in (247mm)

Underglaze blue printed in the centre with a chinoiserie garden scene depicting two figures on a bridge surrounded by a patterned band. The rim decorated with a complex border pattern.

The reverse impressed '*HERCULANEUM*'.

231 MINIATURE PLATE

Earthenware

Herculaneum, Liverpool c.1825

d. 4¾ in (121mm)

Underglaze blue printed with a detail from the 'Indian Views' series, 'View of the Fort, Madura', surrounded by a floral border.

The reverse impressed '*HERCULANEUM*' within a garter surrounding a crown.

232 PLATE

Earthenware

Herculaneum, Liverpool c.1815–25

d. 8½ in (216mm)

Underglaze blue printed with the 'Gate of Mosque of Hafiz Ramut', from the 'Indian Views' series, surrounded by a leaf-patterned border.

The reverse impressed '*HERCULANEUM*'.

233 FROG MUG

Earthenware
Herculaneum, Liverpool c.1815-20

h. 5¼in (133mm)
Underglaze blue printed with a design
from the 'Indian Views' series, 'View of
the Fort, Madura', around the exterior.
A floral border around the inside and
outside rim and down the handle. The
base of the interior with a modelled frog,
painted in green, yellow and orange.

234 PLATE

Earthenware
Herculaneum, Liverpool c.1810-15

d. 10in (253mm)
Underglaze blue printed with the 'View
of the Fort, Madura', from the 'Indian
Views' series, surrounded by a floral
border pattern.
The reverse impressed *'HERCULANEUM'*.

235 BOTTLE

Earthenware
Herculaneum, Liverpool c.1810-20

h. 3¼in (83mm)
Of globular shape with slightly flared
rim and loop handle. Underglaze blue
printed with a design from the 'Indian
Views' series, 'View of the Fort,
Madura', around the exterior, and with a
border pattern around the outside rim
and down the handle.

236 PLATE

Earthenware
Herculaneum, Liverpool c.1830

d. 10in (253mm)
Underglaze blue printed in the centre
with figures, buildings and bridge beside
a river surrounded by a floral border
pattern.
The reverse impressed with the 'Liver bird'
and inscribed *'No 2'*, painted in underglaze blue.

237 PLATE

Earthenware
Herculaneum, Liverpool c.1825-30

d. 6⅝in (168mm)
Underglaze blue printed with a design of
butterflies and foliage and with a narrow
border pattern around the gadrooned rim.
The reverse impressed *'HERCULANEUM'*,
'2' in small type, and *'R'* in larger type.

238 PLATE

Earthenware
Herculaneum, Liverpool c.1830

d. 7¾in (197mm)
Underglaze blue and overglaze enamel
painted with stylised flowers and leaves
in the 'Gaudy Dutch' style and with a
moulded gadrooned rim.
The base impressed with the 'Liver bird'
and painted *'71'* in black.

239 LADLE

Earthenware
Herculaneum, Liverpool c.1830

l. 12³/₈ in (315mm)
Underglaze printed in brown with a
flower and scroll design and with a border
pattern around the inside rim of the
bowl. Further decorated in painted polychrome enamels.

240 TUREEN AND COVER ON STAND, LADLE

Earthenware
Herculaneum, Liverpool c.1830

h. tureen 6¹/₂ in (165mm)
l. ladle 7³/₈ in (187mm)
Underglaze printed in brown with shell,
flowers and scroll pattern and with a
border pattern. Further decorated in
painted polychrome enamels.
The base of the stand impressed with the
'Liver bird' and three dots. '1917' painted
in brown enamel on the base of the
tureen and stand.

241 TUREEN AND COVER

Earthenware
Herculaneum, Liverpool c.1833-5

h. 8¹/₄ in (210mm)
Underglaze blue printed, the tureen
with a view of the Duke of Bridgwater's
Warehouse, Liverpool and with floral
border patterns. The base of the tureen
printed with an octagonal cartouche,
inscribed 'The Dukes / Warehouse. / Liverpool'.
The scene adapted from an engraving of
the same subject from 'Lancashire
Illustrated', published in London in 1832.

143

242 STAND

Earthenware
Herculaneum, Liverpool c.1833–5

l. 7 ¹/₈ in (182mm)
Underglaze blue printed with a view of
the Wellington Rooms, Liverpool, within
a floral border. The reverse printed with
an oblong cartouche inscribed
'Wellington Rooms / Liverpool'.
The reverse impressed with the 'Liver bird'.

243 PLATE

Earthenware
Herculaneum, Liverpool c.1833–5

d. 10¹/₄ in (260mm)
Underglaze blue printed in the centre
with a view of Liverpool surrounded by
a floral border pattern. The reverse
printed with an octagonal cartouche
inscribed *'Liverpool / from the / Seacombe Slip'*.
The reverse with an impressed 'Liver bird'.
The design adapted from an engraving in
'Lancashire Illustrated', published in
London in 1832.

244 JUG

Earthenware
Herculaneum, Liverpool c.1833–5

h. 12in (305mm)
Underglaze printed in black with a view
of Lord Street with St. George's Church
in the distance and with various floral
and border patterns. Underglaze painted
with black banding and with a large bell
below the lip inscribed *'A / PRES'NT
TO THE / ST LUKES SOCIETY / OF
CHANGERINGERS / LIVERPOOL'*

and the motto *'HONI.SOIT.QUI.MAL.Y. PENCE'* (Evil be to him who evil thinks). The view of Lord Street taken from an engraving in *'Lancashire Illustrated'*, published in London in 1832.

245 BUST OF KOSCIUSKO

Stoneware or semi–porcelain
Herculaneum, Liverpool c.1805

h. 8 7/8 in (220mm)
A slip-cast bust of Kosciusko in porcelainous stoneware with traces of gilding. The plinth decorated with emblems of canons and flags and inscribed *'KOSCIUSKO'* on a raised pad. The reverse inscribed in ink.
Kosciusko was a Polish adjutant to Washington.

246 JUG

Stoneware
Herculaneum, Liverpool c.1805–10

h. 6 1/8 in (156mm)
Of oval section in buff stoneware with a chocolate-brown neck and foot. Sprigged with a grape and vine border around the shoulder, various mythological subjects on the body and an acanthus leaf border above the foot.
The base impressed *'HERCULANEUM'*.

247 TEAPOT AND COVER

Stoneware

Herculaneum, Liverpool c.1805

h. 7in (178mm)

Of shaped oval section in cream coloured stoneware covered in a dark purple-brown dip. Decorated with reliefs in cream with figurative subjects around the body and with a border of leaves above the foot and around the shoulder. The cover sprigged with stylised flowers heads.

The base impressed *'HERCULANEUM'*.

248 VASE

Stoneware

Herculaneum, Liverpool c.1805-10

h. 4⅜ in (111mm)

Straight-sided form, slighty tapering to splayed foot and with a cupped rim. Of cream-coloured smear-glazed stoneware with a chocolate-brown dip. Decorated with applied reliefs depicting mythological figures and with an oak leaf and acorn border around the shoulder.

The base impressed *'HERCULANEUM'*.

249 JUG

Stoneware

Herculaneum, Liverpool c.1805

h. 7in (178mm)

Of oval section, slip-cast in a solid marbled body with glazed interior. The exterior decorated with sprigs of mythological subjects, a grape and vine border around

the shoulder and an acanthus leaf border above the foot.
The base impressed *'HERCULANEUM'*.

250 URN
Black basalt
Designed by William Bullock 1805
Probably Herculaneum, Liverpool

h. 8 ¾ in (222mm)
The bowl decorated with screeching winged bat-masks and with mask terminals to the scroll handles. The spreading concave-sided triangular pedestal, centred by comic and tragic masks, on scrolling paw feet. The angles of the base, above the feet, bearing the patent stamp *'W. BULLOCK, / PUB.JULY1, / 1805'*, the underside with a painted number *'79'*.

This patented design by William Bullock of 1805 for a basalt urn reflects the antique style promoted by Thomas Hope's Duchess Street Mansion/Museum in the early 19th century.

251 SUGAR BOX AND COVER
Black basalt
Herculaneum, Liverpool c.1805-10

h. 4 ¾ in (121mm)
Of oval shape, relief-moulded with a border pattern. The sides decorated with sprigs of figurative subjects framed by ribbon-tied leaves alternating with classical figures. The cover with a dolphin knop.
The base impressed *'HERCULANEUM'*.

252 BUST OF WASHINGTON

Stoneware

Herculaneum, Liverpool c.1805

h. 9½ in (241mm)

Slip-cast bust of Washington in buff coloured stoneware, with the American eagle in relief on the pedestal base. The reverse incised *'Washington'* in cursive script along the lower edge of the pedestal. Impressed *'HERCULANEUM'* on the edge of the base.

253 CREAMER

Black basalt

Herculaneum, Liverpool c.1805–10

l. 4in (102mm)

Of oval section with flared lip, moulded in relief with two oval-shaped panels of classical subjects reserved against a basket-weave ground and with a border around the shoulder. Impressed *'HERCULANEUM'* on the footrim.

252

253

254 MUG

Stoneware
Herculaneum, Liverpool c.1805

h. 5in (127mm)
Of straight-sided form in cream coloured stoneware, the interior glazed, and with a band of horizontal grooving below the outside rim. The exterior with sprigged decoration of a drinking party and with a smaller scene of a donkey kicking a fox beneath the handle. Border of acorns and oak leaves above the foot. Impressed *'HERCULANEUM 2'* on the base.

255 JUG

Stoneware
Herculaneum, Liverpool c.1805–10

h. 6½ in (165mm)
Of rounded form on a flared foot in chocolate-brown stoneware and with a foliate lip. The interior glazed. The exterior with sprigged decoration of a goat and 'sporting' putti and with a border of scallop shells above the foot. Impressed *'HERCULANEUM'* on base.

256 TEAPOT AND COVER

Porcelain

Herculaneum, Liverpool 1805

h. 3¾in (95mm)

Painted in iron-red enamel and gilding with a band of overlapping diamonds around the body and on the cover. Further decorated with gilt banding, details on spout and a border pattern around the shoulder. Inscribed *'PW'*, painted in gilt, beneath the spout. The base painted in gilt *'HERCULANEUM / Oct.,2. / 1805'*. This unique painted mark possibly refers to the marriage date of William and Phoebe Smith whose initials appear beneath the spout. William Smith was the manager of the factory from 1810-21.

257 CREAMER

Porcelain

Herculaneum, Liverpool c.1800

h. 3¾in (96mm)

Of silver-shape, overglaze painted in polychrome enamels with a design of 'back-to-back' roses, a number of floral sprigs in pink and various border patterns. Pattern number *'58'* painted in pink enamel on base.

258 TEAPOT AND COVER

Porcelain

Herculaneum, Liverpool c.1815

h. 7in (178mm)

'New oval' shape, overglaze painted with a band of panels of stylised leaves

in red and brown enamels and gilding against a peach ground, further decorated with gilt banding.
Pattern number *'541'* painted in gilt on base.

259 TEAPOT AND COVER, STAND, CREAMER

Porcelain
Herculaneum, Liverpool c.1820–30

h. teapot 6¼in (158mm)
Of oval shape curving in to the base and having a handle with a raised pad.
Painted gilt border patterns of stylised wreaths alternating with vases. Boat-shaped knop to teapot cover.
Pattern number *'1092'* painted in gilt on base.

260 PLANT POTS AND STANDS

Porcelain
Herculaneum, Liverpool c.1810–15

h. 5in (127mm)
A pair of plant pots and stands with dolphin's mask handles. Overglaze decorated in polychrome enamels with gilt border patterns and banding.
Impressed *'HERCULANEUM'*. Pattern number *'300'* painted in gilt on base of stand.

261 VASE

Porcelain

Herculaneum, Liverpool c.1815

h. 8⁷⁄₈in (220mm)

Vase from a garniture, with waisted neck and caryatid handles, standing on a square pedestal which is slightly off-centre. The front painted with flowers in a vase in polychrome enamels and gilding, framed in gilt and reserved against an orange ground. The neck and lower part covered in deep blue, and the whole further lavishly decorated with gilding. Overglaze printed in puce 'HERCULA-NEUM' above a 'Liver bird' and wreath, 'LIVERPOOL' inscribed on a ribboned scroll below.

262 BOUGH POT

Porcelain

Herculaneum, Liverpool 1811

Decorated by W. Dixon, Liverpool

h. 6¾in (172mm)

Shaped bough pot with two scrolled handles and on three claw feet. The front painted with a portrait of a man and child in polychrome enamels. The rest of the pot heavily gilded. Marked on the foot 'Painted by W. Dixon 1811 Liverpool. W. Smith & Child'. The portrait is that of William Smith and his child. William Smith was manager of the pottery from 1810–20. William Dixon was a Liverpool artist working independently for a time at 9 Northumberland Street but was later on the staff of the pottery.

263 COFFEE CAN

Porcelain

Herculaneum, Liverpool c.1815

h. 2⅝in (67mm)

Cylindrical shape having a handle with 'kick' and thumb-rest. Underglaze blue printed with a pagoda pattern around the exterior and with a border around the inside rim, further decorated in gilding.

264 COFFEE CAN

Porcelain

Herculaneum, Liverpool c.1810-15

h. 2⅝in (67mm)

Cylindrical shape having a handle with 'kick' and thumb-rest. Probably decorated by William Dixon with a putto and torch in polychrome enamels with gilt borders and banding. Narrow footrim to base.

265 CREAM EWER AND STAND

Porcelain

Herculaneum, Liverpool c.1815

h. overall 4¾in (121mm)

Painted enamel decoration of floral bouquets on a pink ground with gilding. Overglaze printed in puce on the base with 'HERCULANEUM' above a 'Liver bird' within a wreath, with 'LIVERPOOL' on a scroll below.

266 SUGAR BOX AND COVER

Porcelain

Herculaneum, Liverpool c.1805-10

h. 5 1/8 in (130mm)

Of 'old oval' shape, with mock ring handles. The cover with a 'cushion' knop. The exterior decorated with a continuous landscape, painted in sepia enamel with gilt banding.

Pattern number *'273'* painted in gilt on the base.

267 COFFEE POT AND COVER

Porcelain

Herculaneum, Liverpool c.1815

h. 9 1/2 in (242mm)

Of 'new oval' shape, decorated with black transfer-prints of children playing and with black enamel banding and border patterns. Scroll handle with thumb-rest.